MRS. GRABOWSKA

FOLENS
MATHS
WEEKLY ASSESSMENT

G000140999

Book 6

Hilary Koll

Steve Mills

Folens
Publishers

Introduction

Weekly Assessment and the National Numeracy Framework

Each of the six books in this series provides 34 sharply focused assessments that address the Year's National Numeracy Framework learning objectives. They are arranged in accordance with the five divisions of each yearly teaching programme, and will help teachers to review and record the progress children are making in relation to the learning objectives during each year of school.

The assessments

Assessments consist of either written questions or a mix of written and orally delivered questions, depending on the nature of the objectives. In both cases, the format ensures quick and easy marking.

Assessment administration

Each assessment will take approximately 20–30 minutes of class time, and might follow or conclude the final Mathematics session of the week. Assessments should be selected according to what has been taught in the week. Where an assessment includes oral questions it is recommended that these are delivered at the start and that no more than 5 seconds are given for each question.

Each assessment consists of two pages – a teacher page and a pupil page.

The teacher page includes:

- a list of the learning objectives in a division of the yearly teaching programme to provide overall context, together with the specific objectives assessed in the test (highlighted in bold type) and the related question numbers

- teacher notes that point out typical misconceptions and errors and also offer teaching tips

- oral questions for those tests that include oral work

- answers.

The pupil page is a page with questions and space for answers.

In addition, there is a photocopiable record sheet provided to allow you to record weekly assessment marks for all pupils.

Acknowledgements

Folens allows photocopying of pages marked 'copiable page' for educational use, providing that this use is within the confines of the purchasing institution. Copiable pages should not be declared in any return in respect of any photocopying licence.

Folens books are protected by international copyright laws. All rights are reserved. The copyright of all materials in this book, except where otherwise stated, remains the property of the publisher and authors. No part of this publication may be reproduced, stored in a retrieval system, or transmitted, in any form or by any means, for whatever purpose, without the written permission of Folens Limited.

Hilary Koll and Steve Mills hereby assert their moral rights to be identified as the authors of this work in accordance with the Copyright, Designs and Patents Act 1988.

Editor: Helen Maxey   Layout artist: Philippa Jarvis
Cover design: Ed Gallagher   Illustrations: Susan Hutchison
Cover photograph: Kelvin Freeman (With thanks to Grove Park Primary School, Chiswick.)

© 1999 Folens Limited, on behalf of the authors.

Summary of teaching programme objectives from the *Framework for Teaching Mathematics*, published by the DfEE as part of the National Numeracy Strategy.

First published 1999 by Folens Limited, Dunstable and Dublin.

Folens Limited, Albert House, Apex Business Centre, Boscombe Road, Dunstable, LU5 4RL, United Kingdom.
Reprinted 2000 (twice).

ISBN 186202 827–3

Contents

Place value, ordering and rounding

Activity sheet questions

Written
1–10
- **Multiply and divide decimals mentally by 10 or 100, and integers by 1000, and explain the effect.**
- Use the vocabulary of estimation and approximation. Consolidate rounding an integer to the nearest 10, 100 or 1000.
- Find the difference between a positive and a negative integer, or two negative integers, in a context such as temperature or the number line, and order a set of positive and negative integers.

Teacher note

- Emphasise that each column is worth 10 times more than the column to its right. Columns to the left are larger in value and columns to the right are smaller in value. Using a calculator to multiply and divide by 10, 100 and 1000, and recording the results in columns, may help children see the movement of digits.

Answers

1.
  a. What is 550 multiplied by 10? **5500**
  b. What is 947 divided by 10? **94.7**

2.
  a. What is 640 multiplied by 100? **64 000**
  b. What is 6000 divided by 100? **60**

3.
  a. What is 350 multiplied by 1000? **350 000**
  b. What is 8000 divided by 1000? **8**

4. Finish this sentence:
  'Multiplying by 10, then by 10, then by 10, is the same as multiplying by …' **1000**

5. Write one tenth of 5000. **500**

6. How many times larger than 37 is 37 000? **1000**

7. How many times smaller is 561 than 56 100? **100**

8. How many of these amounts are there in £8000?
  a. £10 **800**   b. £100 **80**   c. £1000 **8**

9.
  a. 0.7 x 10 = **7**   b. 47 x **100** = 4700   c. **1000** x 6.2 = 6200

10.
  a. 6 ÷ 10 = **0.6**   b. 6300 ÷ **1000** = 6.3   c. **48** ÷ 100 = 0.48

Name: _____   Date: _____

Place value, ordering and rounding

1

a. What is 550 multiplied by 10?

b. What is 947 divided by 10?

2

a. What is 640 multiplied by 100?

b. What is 6000 divided by 100?

3

a. What is 350 multiplied by 1000?

b. What is 8000 divided by 1000?

4

Finish this sentence:

'Multiplying by 10, then by 10, then by 10,
is the same as multiplying by …'

5 Write one tenth of 5000.

6 How many times larger than 37 is 37 000?

7 How many times smaller is 561 than 56 100?

8 How many of these amounts are there in £8000?

a. £10 _____   b. £100 _____   c. £1000 _____

9 a. 0.7 x 10 = _____   b. 47 x _____ = 4700   c. _____ x 6.2 = 6200

10 a. 6 ÷ 10 = _____   b. 6300 ÷ _____ = 6.3   c. _____ ÷ 100 = 0.48

© Folens (copiable page)

ASSESSMENT

2

Place value, ordering and rounding

Activity sheet questions

Written 1–8

○ Multiply and divide decimals mentally by 10 or 100, and integers by 1000, and explain the effect.

● **Use the vocabulary of estimation and approximation.**
Consolidate rounding an integer to the nearest 10, 100 or 1000.

○ Find the difference between a positive and a negative integer, or two negative integers, in a context such as temperature or the number line, and order a set of positive and negative integers.

Teacher note

● Children's rounding skills will be improved by the use of number lines, e.g. 0 _ _ _ _ _ _ _ _ 1000, marked in hundreds. Mark a 3-digit number on the line, such as 832, and it can be clearly seen which hundred it is nearest to.

Answers

1   a. Tick approximately how many playing cards in a line will stretch for 1 kilometre.

  10 ☐   100 ☐   1000 ☐   10 000 ✓

b. How do you know?

> e.g. 1 card = approx. 10cm long, so 10 cards = approx 1m. 1km = 1000m, so 10 x 1000 = 10 000

2   a. Estimate how many times your heart beats in an hour.

  40 ☐   400 ☐   4000 ✓   40 000 ☐

b. How do you know?

> e.g. Approx. 70 beats/minute. 60 minutes = 1 hour, so 70 x 60 = 4200 = approx. 4000

3   Which numbers do you think are being pointed to?

(Answers close to these values are acceptable.)

  0 ↓   ↓   ↓   ↓ 10 000

  2000   **6000**   **9000**

4   Join the numbers in the boxes to the number line.

(Answers close to these values are acceptable.)

  −100 ——————————————— 0

  −25   **−90**   **−5**

5   Which numbers do you think are being pointed to?

(Answers close to these values are acceptable.)

  0 ↓   ↓   ↓   1

  0.1   **0.3**   **0.8**

6   Round these numbers to the nearest 100.   a. 365 **400**   b. 8632 **8600**

7   Round these numbers to the nearest 1000.   a. 4106 **4000**   b. 90 823 **91 000**

8   Tick the best approximation for 30.7 + 61.9.

  307 + 619 ☐   30 + 60 ☐   31 + 62 ✓

6

Name: _____   Date: _____

Place value, ordering and rounding

1

a. Tick approximately how many playing cards in a line will stretch for 1 kilometre.

10 ☐   100 ☐   1000 ☐   10 000 ☐

b. How do you know?

☐

2

a. Estimate how many times your heart beats in an hour.

40 ☐   400 ☐   4000 ☐   40 000 ☐

b. How do you know?

☐

3 Which numbers do you think are being pointed to?

0 __↓_____↓_____↓__ 10 000

☐   ☐   ☐

4 Join the numbers in the boxes to the number line.

−100   0

−25   −90   −5

5 Which numbers do you think are being pointed to?

0 _↓_____↓_____↓_ 1

☐   ☐   ☐

6 Round these numbers to the nearest 100.   a. 365 ☐   b. 8632 ☐

7 Round these numbers to the nearest 1000.   a. 4106 ☐   b. 90 823 ☐

8 Tick the best approximation for 30.7 + 61.9.

307 + 619 ☐   30 + 60 ☐   31 + 62 ☐

Place value, ordering and rounding

Activity sheet questions

- Multiply and divide decimals mentally by 10 or 100, and integers by 1000, and explain the effect.
- Use the vocabulary of estimation and approximation.
  Consolidate rounding an integer to the nearest 10, 100 or 1000.

Written 1–7

- **Find the difference between a positive and a negative integer, or two negative integers, in a context such as temperature or the number line, and order a set of positive and negative integers.**

Teacher note

- Children often require plenty of practice in adding and subtracting through zero with the aid of visual support before having the confidence to work abstractly.

Answers to question 2

Possible answers for:
balloon 2. –8, –7, –6, –5, –4, –3
balloon 4. 0, 1, 2
balloon 6. Any number greater than 3.

Answers

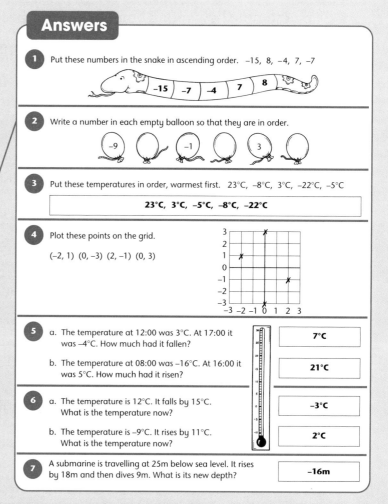

1 Put these numbers in the snake in ascending order. –15, 8, –4, 7, –7

   –15 –7 –4 7 8

2 Write a number in each empty balloon so that they are in order.

   –9   –1   3

3 Put these temperatures in order, warmest first. 23°C, –8°C, 3°C, –22°C, –5°C

   23°C, 3°C, –5°C, –8°C, –22°C

4 Plot these points on the grid.

   (–2, 1) (0, –3) (2, –1) (0, 3)

5 a. The temperature at 12:00 was 3°C. At 17:00 it was –4°C. How much had it fallen?   **7°C**

   b. The temperature at 08:00 was –16°C. At 16:00 it was 5°C. How much had it risen?   **21°C**

6 a. The temperature is 12°C. It falls by 15°C. What is the temperature now?   **–3°C**

   b. The temperature is –9°C. It rises by 11°C. What is the temperature now?   **2°C**

7 A submarine is travelling at 25m below sea level. It rises by 18m and then dives 9m. What is its new depth?   **–16m**

Name: _____   Date: _____

1 Put these numbers in the snake in ascending order. −15, 8, −4, 7, −7

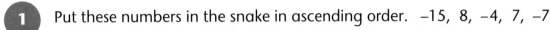

2 Write a number in each empty balloon so that they are in order.

3 Put these temperatures in order, warmest first. 23°C, −8°C, 3°C, −22°C, −5°C

4 Plot these points on the grid.

(−2, 1) (0, −3) (2, −1) (0, 3)

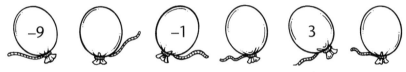

5 a. The temperature at 12:00 was 3°C. At 17:00 it was −4°C. How much had it fallen?

b. The temperature at 08:00 was −16°C. At 16:00 it was 5°C. How much had it risen?

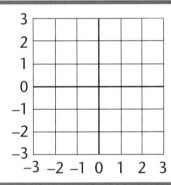

6 a. The temperature is 12°C. It falls by 15°C. What is the temperature now?

b. The temperature is −9°C. It rises by 11°C. What is the temperature now?

7 A submarine is travelling at 25m below sea level. It rises by 18m and then dives 9m. What is its new depth?

Activity sheet questions

Oral

1–6 ● Recognise squares of numbers to at least 12 x 12.

7–10 ● Make general statements about odd or even numbers, including the outcome of products.

Written

1–7 ● Recognise and extend number sequences, such as the sequence of square numbers, or the sequence of triangular numbers 1, 3, 6, 10, 15 …
Count on in steps of 0.1, 0.2, 0.25, 0.5 … , and then back.

● Recognise multiples up to 10 x 10.
Know and apply simple tests of divisibility.
Find simple common multiples.

● Recognise prime numbers to at least 20.

● Factorise numbers to 100 into prime factors.

Teacher note

● Children need to understand that it is the unit's digit that determines whether a number is odd or even, however large the number.

● The term 'product' means the result of multiplication.

Oral questions

1. What is 8 times 8?
2. What is 7 multiplied by 7?
3. What is the square of 9?
4. What is 10 squared?
5. What number multiplied by itself gives 132?
6. What is the area of a square of which one side is 12m?

Write whether each of these is true or false:

7. The sum of three odd numbers is odd.
8. The difference between an odd number and an even number is even.
9. The product of an even number and an odd number is odd.
10. The product of two odd numbers is odd.

Answers

1.	**64**	6.	**144m²**
2.	**49**	7.	**true**
3.	**81**	8.	**false**
4.	**100**	9.	**false**
5.	**11**	10.	**true**

1 Write the next four numbers in this sequence. 32, 40, 48 …   **56, 64, 72, 80**

2 Write the next six numbers in this sequence. 31, 42, 53 …
64, 75, 86, 97, 108, 119

3 Write the next six numbers in the carriages.
0.5 | 1.0 | 1.5 | **2.0** | **2.5** | **3.0** | **3.5** | **4.0** | **4.5**

4 Fill in the missing numbers.   1   3   **6**   10   **15**   21

5 Fill in the missing numbers in the bottles.
10   29   **48**   **67**   86   **105**

6 Continue the pattern in the path.
163   142   121   **100**   **79**   58   **37**   16

7 Fill in the bricks.   −45   −36   **−27**   **−18**   −9

10

Name: _____   Date: _____

1.	6.
2.	7.
3.	8.
4.	9.
5.	10.

1 Write the next four numbers in this sequence. 32, 40, 48 …

2 Write the next six numbers in this sequence. 31, 42, 53 …

3 Write the next six numbers in the carriages.

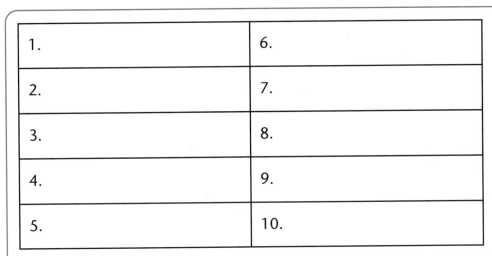

0.5   1.0   1.5

4 Fill in the missing numbers.   1   3   ☐   10   ☐   21

5 Fill in the missing numbers in the bottles.

10   29   86

6 Continue the pattern in the path.

163   142   121

7 Fill in the bricks.   –45   –36   ☐   ☐   –9

Activity sheet questions

- Recognise squares of numbers to at least 12 x 12.
- Make general statements about odd or even numbers, including the outcome of products.
- Recognise and extend number sequences, such as the sequence of square numbers or the sequence of triangular numbers 1, 3, 6, 10, 15 …
  Count on in steps of 0.1, 0.2, 0.25, 0.5 … , and then back.

Written
1–6
- Recognise multiples up to 10 x 10.
  Know and apply simple tests of divisibility.
  Find simple common multiples.
7–8
- **Recognise prime numbers to at least 20.**
9
  Factorise numbers to 100 into prime factors.

Teacher note

- It should be noted that 1 is not regarded as a prime number, since it has only one factor. Prime numbers have two factors, therefore 2 is regarded as the first (and only even) prime number.

Answers to question 6
Possible answers include:
12, 24, 36, 48, 60, 72, 84, 96, 108, 120, 132 …

Answers

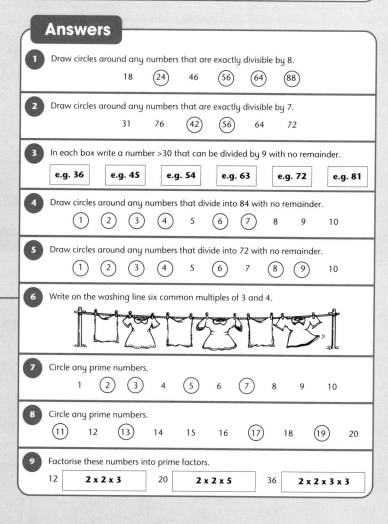

1 Draw circles around any numbers that are exactly divisible by 8.
18 (24) 46 (56) (64) (88)

2 Draw circles around any numbers that are exactly divisible by 7.
31 76 (42) (56) 64 72

3 In each box write a number >30 that can be divided by 9 with no remainder.
e.g. 36 | e.g. 45 | e.g. 54 | e.g. 63 | e.g. 72 | e.g. 81

4 Draw circles around any numbers that divide into 84 with no remainder.
(1) (2) (3) (4) 5 (6) (7) 8 9 10

5 Draw circles around any numbers that divide into 72 with no remainder.
(1) (2) (3) (4) 5 (6) 7 (8) (9) 10

6 Write on the washing line six common multiples of 3 and 4.

7 Circle any prime numbers.
1 (2) (3) 4 (5) 6 (7) 8 9 10

8 Circle any prime numbers.
(11) 12 (13) 14 15 16 (17) 18 (19) 20

9 Factorise these numbers into prime factors.
12 | 2 x 2 x 3 | 20 | 2 x 2 x 5 | 36 | 2 x 2 x 3 x 3

Name: _____   Date: _____

1 Draw circles around any numbers that are exactly divisible by 8.

        18   24   46   56   64   88

2 Draw circles around any numbers that are exactly divisible by 7.

        31   76   42   56   64   72

3 In each box write a number >30 that can be divided by 9 with no remainder.

[ ]   [ ]   [ ]   [ ]   [ ]   [ ]

4 Draw circles around any numbers that divide into 84 with no remainder.

   1   2   3   4   5   6   7   8   9   10

5 Draw circles around any numbers that divide into 72 with no remainder.

   1   2   3   4   5   6   7   8   9   10

6 Write on the washing line six common multiples of 3 and 4.

7 Circle any prime numbers.

   1   2   3   4   5   6   7   8   9   10

8 Circle any prime numbers.

11   12   13   14   15   16   17   18   19   20

9 Factorise these numbers into prime factors.

12 [ ]   20 [ ]   36 [ ]

ASSESSMENT 6

Fractions

Activity sheet questions

Written

1–2 ● Change a fraction such as $\frac{33}{8}$ to the equivalent mixed number $4\frac{1}{8}$, and vice versa.

3–4 Reduce a fraction to its simplest form by cancelling common factors in the numerator and denominator.

5–10 Recognise relationships between fractions: for example, that $\frac{1}{10}$ is ten times $\frac{1}{100}$, and $\frac{1}{16}$ is half of $\frac{1}{8}$.

● Order fractions such as $\frac{2}{3}$, $\frac{3}{4}$ and $\frac{5}{6}$ by converting them to fractions with a common denominator, and position them on a number line.

● Use a fraction as an 'operator' to find fractions, including tenths and hundredths, of numbers or quantities. (e.g. $\frac{5}{8}$ of 32, $\frac{7}{10}$ of 40, $\frac{9}{100}$ of 400 centimetres).

● Solve simple problems involving ratio and proportion.

Teacher note

● It may be necessary to explain the difference between a proper fraction, which has a numerator that is smaller than the denominator (e.g. $\frac{1}{2}$) and a value of less than 1, and an improper fraction, where the opposite is true (e.g. $\frac{6}{5}$).

● Children need a sound understanding of equivalence before they can fully appreciate the cancelling process. Continue to provide visual reinforcement when considering the relationships between fractions, as children find these ideas difficult.

Answers to questions 3 and 4

Lowest equivalent fractions (as shown) are preferred but the following answers are also correct:

3b. $\frac{4}{10}$ 4a. $\frac{5}{15}$ or $\frac{3}{9}$ 4b. $\frac{9}{12}$ 4c. $\frac{6}{10}$

Answers

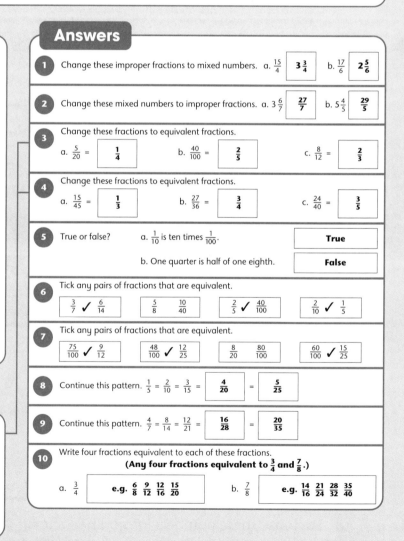

1 Change these improper fractions to mixed numbers.   a. $\frac{15}{4}$ **$3\frac{3}{4}$**   b. $\frac{17}{6}$ **$2\frac{5}{6}$**

2 Change these mixed numbers to improper fractions.   a. $3\frac{6}{7}$ **$\frac{27}{7}$**   b. $5\frac{4}{5}$ **$\frac{29}{5}$**

3 Change these fractions to equivalent fractions.
a. $\frac{5}{20}$ = **$\frac{1}{4}$**   b. $\frac{40}{100}$ = **$\frac{2}{5}$**   c. $\frac{8}{12}$ = **$\frac{2}{3}$**

4 Change these fractions to equivalent fractions.
a. $\frac{15}{45}$ = **$\frac{1}{3}$**   b. $\frac{27}{36}$ = **$\frac{3}{4}$**   c. $\frac{24}{40}$ = **$\frac{3}{5}$**

5 True or false?   a. $\frac{1}{10}$ is ten times $\frac{1}{100}$.   **True**
   b. One quarter is half of one eighth.   **False**

6 Tick any pairs of fractions that are equivalent.
$\frac{3}{7}$ ✓ $\frac{6}{14}$ $\frac{5}{8}$ $\frac{10}{40}$ $\frac{2}{5}$ ✓ $\frac{40}{100}$ $\frac{2}{10}$ ✓ $\frac{1}{5}$

7 Tick any pairs of fractions that are equivalent.
$\frac{75}{100}$ ✓ $\frac{9}{12}$ $\frac{48}{100}$ ✓ $\frac{12}{25}$ $\frac{8}{20}$ $\frac{80}{100}$ $\frac{60}{100}$ ✓ $\frac{15}{25}$

8 Continue this pattern. $\frac{1}{5} = \frac{2}{10} = \frac{3}{15} = $ **$\frac{4}{20}$** = **$\frac{5}{25}$**

9 Continue this pattern. $\frac{4}{7} = \frac{8}{14} = \frac{12}{21} = $ **$\frac{16}{28}$** = **$\frac{20}{35}$**

10 Write four fractions equivalent to each of these fractions.
(Any four fractions equivalent to $\frac{3}{4}$ and $\frac{7}{8}$.)
a. $\frac{3}{4}$ **e.g. $\frac{6}{8}$ $\frac{9}{12}$ $\frac{12}{16}$ $\frac{15}{20}$**   b. $\frac{7}{8}$ **e.g. $\frac{14}{16}$ $\frac{21}{24}$ $\frac{28}{32}$ $\frac{35}{40}$**

Name: _____ Date: _____

Fractions

---

1 Change these improper fractions to mixed numbers. a. $\frac{15}{4}$ ☐ b. $\frac{17}{6}$ ☐

---

2 Change these mixed numbers to improper fractions. a. $3\frac{6}{7}$ ☐ b. $5\frac{4}{5}$ ☐

---

3 Change these fractions to equivalent fractions.

a. $\frac{5}{20}$ = ☐   b. $\frac{40}{100}$ = ☐   c. $\frac{8}{12}$ = ☐

---

4 Change these fractions to equivalent fractions.

a. $\frac{15}{45}$ = ☐   b. $\frac{27}{36}$ = ☐   c. $\frac{24}{40}$ = ☐

---

5 True or false?   a. $\frac{1}{10}$ is ten times $\frac{1}{100}$. ☐

b. One quarter is half of one eighth. ☐

---

6 Tick any pairs of fractions that are equivalent.

| $\frac{3}{7}$ $\frac{6}{14}$ | $\frac{5}{8}$ $\frac{10}{40}$ | $\frac{2}{5}$ $\frac{40}{100}$ | $\frac{2}{10}$ $\frac{1}{5}$ |

---

7 Tick any pairs of fractions that are equivalent.

| $\frac{75}{100}$ $\frac{9}{12}$ | $\frac{48}{100}$ $\frac{12}{25}$ | $\frac{8}{20}$ $\frac{80}{100}$ | $\frac{60}{100}$ $\frac{15}{25}$ |

---

8 Continue this pattern. $\frac{1}{5}$ = $\frac{2}{10}$ = $\frac{3}{15}$ = ☐ = ☐

---

9 Continue this pattern. $\frac{4}{7}$ = $\frac{8}{14}$ = $\frac{12}{21}$ = ☐ = ☐

---

10 Write four fractions equivalent to each of these fractions.

a. $\frac{3}{4}$ ☐   b. $\frac{7}{8}$ ☐

© Folens (copiable page)

Activity sheet questions

- Change a fraction such as $\frac{33}{8}$ to the equivalent mixed number $4\frac{1}{8}$, and vice versa.

  Reduce a fraction to its simplest form by cancelling common factors in the numerator and denominator.

  Recognise relationships between fractions: for example, that $\frac{1}{10}$ is ten times $\frac{1}{100}$, and $\frac{1}{16}$ is half of $\frac{1}{8}$.

Oral

1–10
- **Use a fraction as an 'operator' to find fractions, including tenths and hundredths, of numbers or quantities (e.g. $\frac{5}{8}$ of 32, $\frac{7}{10}$ of 40, $\frac{9}{100}$ of 400 centimetres).**

Written

1–3
- **Order fractions such as $\frac{2}{3}$, $\frac{3}{4}$ and $\frac{5}{6}$ by converting them to fractions with a common denominator, and position them on a number line.**

4–5
- **Solve simple problems involving ratio and proportion.**

Teacher note

- A number line from 0 to 1, showing the position of fractions and their relationships, should be available for children to use.

Oral questions

1. How many halves are there in $2\frac{1}{2}$?
2. How many quarters are there in $3\frac{3}{4}$?
3. How many thirds are there in $4\frac{1}{3}$?
4. What is three tenths of 60?
5. What is nine tenths of 50?
6. Write $\frac{7}{10}$ of 2 metres in centimetres.
7. Write $\frac{60}{100}$ of 3 kilograms in grams.
8. What fraction of £1 is 68p?
   (Do not write as a decimal.)
9. What fraction of 1 litre is 265ml?
   (Do not write as a decimal.)
10. What fraction of 1 year that is not a leap year is two days?
    (Do not write as a decimal.)

Answers

1. **5**	6. **140cm**
2. **15**	7. **1800g**
3. **13**	8. **$\frac{68}{100}$ (or $\frac{34}{50}$ or $\frac{17}{25}$)**
4. **18**	9. **$\frac{265}{1000}$ (or $\frac{53}{200}$)**
5. **45**	10. **$\frac{2}{365}$**

1 Write these fractions on the labels in order of size, smallest fraction first.

$\frac{1}{2}, \frac{1}{3}, \frac{3}{4}, \frac{2}{3}, \frac{1}{4}$ [cans labelled $\frac{1}{4}$ $\frac{1}{3}$ $\frac{1}{2}$ $\frac{2}{3}$ $\frac{3}{4}$]

2 Mark these fractions on the number line. $\frac{3}{4}, \frac{1}{6}, \frac{2}{3}, \frac{7}{12}$

0 —— $\frac{1}{6}$ —————— $\frac{7}{12}$ $\frac{2}{3}$ $\frac{3}{4}$ ———— 1

3 Write these mixed numbers in order, largest first. $1\frac{7}{10}, 2\frac{3}{5}, 2\frac{1}{20}, 1\frac{3}{4}, 2\frac{7}{10}$

$$2\frac{7}{10},\ 2\frac{3}{5},\ 2\frac{1}{20},\ 1\frac{3}{4},\ 1\frac{7}{10}$$

4 Look at these two shapes.

a. How many shaded squares to white squares? | **2 to 5**

b. What proportion of the total number of squares is shaded? | $\frac{2}{7}$

c. What fraction of the large shape is the small one? | $\frac{2}{5}$

5 In a packet of chewy sweets there are 4 yellow sweets to every 9 blue sweets.

a. How many yellow sweets will there be to every 27 blue sweets? | **12**

b. How many blue sweets will there be to every 24 yellow sweets? | **54**

A packet contains 52 sweets. c. How many sweets will be blue? | **36**

d. How many sweets will be yellow? | **16**

Name: _____ Date: _____

1.	6.
2.	7.
3.	8.
4.	9.
5.	10.

1 Write these fractions on the labels in order of size, smallest fraction first.

$\frac{1}{2}$, $\frac{1}{3}$, $\frac{3}{4}$, $\frac{2}{3}$, $\frac{1}{4}$

2 Mark these fractions on the number line. $\frac{3}{4}$, $\frac{1}{6}$, $\frac{2}{3}$, $\frac{7}{12}$

0   1

3 Write these mixed numbers in order, largest first. $1\frac{7}{10}$, $2\frac{3}{5}$, $2\frac{1}{20}$, $1\frac{3}{4}$, $2\frac{7}{10}$

4 Look at these two shapes.

  a. How many shaded squares to white squares?

  b. What proportion of the total number of squares is shaded?

  c. What fraction of the large shape is the small one?

5 In a packet of chewy sweets there are 4 yellow sweets to every 9 blue sweets.

  a. How many yellow sweets will there be to every 27 blue sweets?

  b. How many blue sweets will there be to every 24 yellow sweets?

A packet contains 52 sweets. c. How many sweets will be blue?

  d. How many sweets will be yellow?

Fractions

Activity sheet questions

Written

1–3 ● Use decimal notation for tenths and hundredths in calculations, and tenths, hundredths and thousandths when recording measurements.

4 Know what each digit represents in a number with up to three decimal places.

5–6 Order a mixed set of numbers or measurements with up to three decimal places.

7 Give a decimal fraction lying between two others (e.g. between 3.4 and 3.5).

● Round a number with two decimal places to the nearest tenth or to the nearest whole number.

● Recognise the equivalence between the decimal and fraction forms of one half, one quarter, three quarters, one eighth… and tenths, hundredths and thousandths (e.g. $\frac{700}{1000} = \frac{70}{100} = \frac{7}{10} = 0.7$).
Begin to convert a fraction to a decimal using division.

● Understand percentage as the number of parts in every 100.
Express simple fractions such as one half, one quarter, three quarters, one third, two thirds…, and tenths and hundredths, as percentages (e.g. know that $\frac{1}{3} = 33\frac{1}{3}\%$).
Find simple percentages of small whole-number quantities (e.g. find 10% of £500, then 20%, 40% and 80% by doubling).

Teacher note

● Children often use a 'longer is larger' strategy when ordering decimals, thus giving 0.75 as larger than 0.8. Further work on the value of the columns after the decimal point may be necessary.

Answers to question 7

Possible answers include:

a. 6.581, 6.582, 6.583, 6.584, 6.585, 6.586, 6.587, 6.588

b. 7.031, 7.032, 7.034

c. 12.671, 12.672, 12.673, 12.674, 12.675, 12.676, 12.677, 12.678, 12.679.

Answers

1 Write these numbers in words.

a. 0.82   **Nought point eight two**

b. 6.71   **Six point seven one**

c. 0.562   **Nought point five six two**

2 Use digits to write these numbers.

a. Six point five three   **6.53**

b. Twelve point six four one   **12.641**

c. Five and twenty-six hundredths   **5.26**

d. Two and three tenths, four hundredths and eight thousandths   **2.348**

3 Write which measurements are being pointed to on this scale.

4.23kg   ↓   ↓   ↓ 4.24kg

4.232kg   **4.235kg**   **4.239kg**

4 Write what each underlined digit is worth.

a. 8.5̲6   **5 tenths**   b. 4.8̲9   **9 hundredths**   c. 34.50̲4   **4 thousandths**

5 Put these decimals in order, largest first.

6.34, 7.38, 6.28, 6.04, 7.15   **7.38, 7.15, 6.34, 6.28, 6.04**

6 Put these measurements in order, smallest first.

8.464m, 7.798m, 8.45m, 7.901m, 7.87m   **7.798m, 7.87m, 7.901m, 8.45m, 8.464m**

7 Write a decimal fraction that lies between these numbers.

a. 6.58 and 6.59   b. 7.03 and 7.04   c. 12.67 and 12.68

Name: _____ Date: _____

Fractions

1 Write these numbers in words.

b. 6.71 [_____]

a. 0.82 [_____]

c. 0.562 [_____]

2 Use digits to write these numbers.

a. Six point five three

[_____]

b. Twelve point six four one

[_____]

c. Five and twenty-six hundredths

[_____]

d. Two and three tenths, four hundredths and eight thousandths

[_____]

3 Write which measurements are being pointed to on this scale.

4.23kg ↓ ↓ ↓ 4.24kg

[_____] [_____] [_____]

4 Write what each underlined digit is worth.

a. 8.<u>5</u>6 [_____] b. 4.8<u>9</u> [_____] c. 34.50<u>4</u> [_____]

5 Put these decimals in order, largest first.

6.34, 7.38, 6.28, 6.04, 7.15 [_____]

6 Put these measurements in order, smallest first.

8.464m, 7.798m, 8.45m, 7.901m, 7.87m [_____]

7 Write a decimal fraction that lies between these numbers.

a. 6.58 and 6.59 [_____] b. 7.03 and 7.04 [_____] c. 12.67 and 12.68 [_____]

Fractions

Activity sheet questions

○ Use decimal notation for tenths and hundredths in calculations, and tenths, hundredths and thousandths when recording measurements.
Know what each digit represents in a number with up to three decimal places.
Order a mixed set of numbers or measurements with up to three decimal places.
Give a decimal fraction lying between two others (e.g. between 3.4 and 3.5).

Oral
1–10

● **Round a number with two decimal places to the nearest tenth or to the nearest whole number.**

Written
1–6

● **Recognise the equivalence between the decimal and fraction forms of one half, one quarter, three quarters, one eighth… and tenths, hundredths and thousandths (e.g. $\frac{700}{1000} = \frac{70}{100} = \frac{7}{10} = 0.7$).**
Begin to convert a fraction to a decimal using division.

○ Understand percentage as the number of parts in every 100.
Express simple fractions such as one half, one quarter, three quarters, one third, two thirds…, and tenths and hundredths, as percentages (e.g. know that $\frac{1}{3} = 33\frac{1}{3}\%$).
Find simple percentages of small whole-number quantities (e.g. find 10% of £500, then 20%, 40% and 80% by doubling).

Teacher note

● Provide children with number lines showing tenths and hundredths for rounding work.

Oral questions

Round these decimals to the nearest whole number:
1. 15.8
2. 19.5
3. 54.46
4. 34.59

Round these decimals to the nearest tenth:
5. 3.46
6. 7.39
7. 6.75
8. 10.04
9. What is 4.62 to one decimal place?
10. What is 8.29 to one decimal place?

Answers

1.	**16**	6.	**7.4**
2.	**20**	7.	**6.8**
3.	**54**	8.	**10.0**
4.	**35**	9.	**4.6**
5.	**3.5**	10.	**8.3**

1 Write an equivalent fraction for each of these decimals.

a. 0.5   **e.g. $\frac{1}{2}$**   b. 0.25   **e.g. $\frac{1}{4}$**   c. 0.75   **e.g. $\frac{3}{4}$**   d. 0.125   **e.g. $\frac{1}{8}$**

2 Write the equivalent decimal for each of these fractions.

a. $\frac{7}{100}$ **0.07**   b. $\frac{1}{10}$ **0.1**   c. $\frac{45}{100}$ **0.45**   d. $\frac{15}{1000}$ **0.015**

3 Tick the decimal that is equal to $\frac{247}{1000}$.

a 24.7 ☐   b. 247.0 ☐   c. 0.247 ✓   d. 2.47 ☐

4 Tick the mixed number that is equal to 6.938.

a. $6\frac{93}{8}$ ☐   b. $6\frac{938}{100}$ ☐   c. $6\frac{938}{1000}$ ✓

5 Write these measurements as decimals.

a. $8\frac{54}{100}$ cm   **8.54cm**   b. $7\frac{427}{1000}$ kg   **7.427kg**

6 Write these measurements as mixed numbers.

a. 43.39secs   **$43\frac{39}{100}$ secs**   b. 51.892cm   **$51\frac{892}{1000}$ cm**

Name: _____   Date: _____

1.	6.
2.	7.
3.	8.
4.	9.
5.	10.

1   Write an equivalent fraction for each of these decimals.

a. 0.5 [ ]   b. 0.25 [ ]   c. 0.75 [ ]   d. 0.125 [ ]

2   Write the equivalent decimal for each of these fractions.

a. $\frac{7}{100}$ [ ]   b. $\frac{1}{10}$ [ ]   c. $\frac{45}{100}$ [ ]   d. $\frac{15}{1000}$ [ ]

3   Tick the decimal that is equal to $\frac{247}{1000}$.

a 24.7 [ ]   b. 247.0 [ ]   c. 0.247 [ ]   d. 2.47 [ ]

4   Tick the mixed number that is equal to 6.938.

a. $6\frac{93}{8}$ [ ]   b. $6\frac{938}{100}$ [ ]   c. $6\frac{938}{1000}$ [ ]

5   Write these measurements as decimals.

a. $8\frac{54}{100}$ cm [ ]   b. $7\frac{427}{1000}$ kg [ ]

6   Write these measurements as mixed numbers.

a. 43.39secs [ ]   b. 51.892cm [ ]

Fractions

Activity sheet questions

- Use decimal notation for tenths and hundredths in calculations, and tenths, hundredths and thousandths when recording measurements.
  Know what each digit represents in a number with up to three decimal places.
  Order a mixed set of numbers or measurements with up to three decimal places.
  Give a decimal fraction lying between two others.
- Round a number with two decimal places to the nearest tenth or to the nearest whole number.
- Recognise the equivalence between the decimal and fraction forms of one half, one quarter, three quarters, one eighth … and tenths, hundredths and thousandths (e.g. $\frac{700}{1000} = \frac{70}{100} = \frac{7}{10} = 0.7$).
  Begin to convert a fraction to a decimal using division.

Written

1 ● **Understand percentage as the number of parts in every 100.**

2–5 **Express simple fractions such as one half, one quarter, three quarters, one third, two thirds…, and tenths and hundredths, as percentages.**

6–8 **Find simple percentages of small whole-number quantities.**

Teacher note

- Building percentage work on sound decimal and fraction foundations is vital. Children can then see percentages as simple fractions with a denominator of 100.

Answers

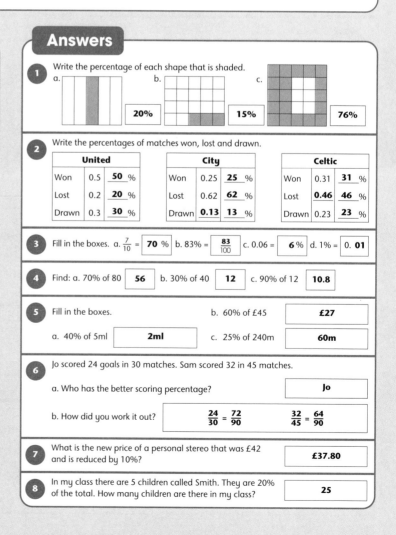

1 Write the percentage of each shape that is shaded.
  a. **20%** b. **15%** c. **76%**

2 Write the percentages of matches won, lost and drawn.

United			City			Celtic		
Won	0.5	**50** %	Won	0.25	**25** %	Won	0.31	**31** %
Lost	0.2	**20** %	Lost	0.62	**62** %	Lost	**0.46**	**46** %
Drawn	0.3	**30** %	Drawn	**0.13**	**13** %	Drawn	0.23	**23** %

3 Fill in the boxes. a. $\frac{7}{10}$ = **70** % b. 83% = **$\frac{83}{100}$** c. 0.06 = **6** % d. 1% = 0. **01**

4 Find: a. 70% of 80 **56** b. 30% of 40 **12** c. 90% of 12 **10.8**

5 Fill in the boxes. b. 60% of £45 **£27**
  a. 40% of 5ml **2ml** c. 25% of 240m **60m**

6 Jo scored 24 goals in 30 matches. Sam scored 32 in 45 matches.
  a. Who has the better scoring percentage? **Jo**
  b. How did you work it out? $\frac{24}{30} = \frac{72}{90}$ $\frac{32}{45} = \frac{64}{90}$

7 What is the new price of a personal stereo that was £42 and is reduced by 10%? **£37.80**

8 In my class there are 5 children called Smith. They are 20% of the total. How many children are there in my class? **25**

Name: _____   Date: _____

Fractions

1 Write the percentage of each shape that is shaded.

a.

b.

c.

2 Write the percentages of matches won, lost and drawn.

United		
Won	0.5	_____ %
Lost	0.2	_____ %
Drawn	0.3	_____ %

City		
Won	0.25	_____ %
Lost	0.62	_____ %
Drawn	_____	_____ %

Celtic		
Won	0.31	_____ %
Lost	_____	_____ %
Drawn	0.23	_____ %

3 Fill in the boxes. a. $\frac{7}{10}$ = ☐ % b. 83% = $\frac{☐}{100}$ c. 0.06 = ☐ % d. 1% = 0.☐

4 Find: a. 70% of 80 ☐   b. 30% of 40 ☐   c. 90% of 12 ☐

5 Fill in the boxes.   b. 60% of £45 ☐

   a. 40% of 5ml ☐   c. 25% of 240m ☐

6 Jo scored 24 goals in 30 matches. Sam scored 32 in 45 matches.

   a. Who has the better scoring percentage? ☐

   b. How did you work it out? ☐

7 What is the new price of a personal stereo that was £42 and is reduced by 10%? ☐

8 In my class there are 5 children called Smith. They are 20% of the total. How many children are there in my class? ☐

Mental calculation strategies (+ and –)

Activity sheet questions

Written

1–4
5–8

- Consolidate all strategies from previous year including:
  - find a difference by counting up
  - add or subtract the nearest multiple of 10, 100 or 1000, then adjust
  - use the relationship between addition and subtraction
  - add several numbers.
- Use known number facts and place value to consolidate mental addition and subtraction. (e.g. 470 + 380, 810 – 380, 7.4 + 9.8, 9.2 – 8.6).

Teacher note

- The ability to partition effectively is a good indicator of children's understanding of place value. Children need experience of using place value cards when partitioning, and should be encouraged to check their answers by approximating. When adding and subtracting near doubles using decimals, children often make errors by treating the final tenth as a whole number, e.g. 4.7 + 4.8 = (4.7 x 2) + 1, instead of as a decimal, e.g. 4.7 + 4.8 = (4.7 x 2) + 0.1.

Answers

1. a. 72 – 48 =   **24**   b. 104 – 89 =   **15**

2. a. 207 – 186 =   **21**   b. 608 – 489 =   **119**

3. a. 2000 – 1952 =   **48**   b. 4000 – 2875 =   **1125**

4. a. 7000 – 5994 =   **1006**   b. 8000 – 3996 =   **4004**

5. a. 135 + 41 =   **176**   b. 261 + 186 =   **447**

6. a. 4206 + 3007 =   **7213**   b. 5723 + 3992 =   **9715**

7. a. 362 – 159 =   **203**   b. 541 – 298 =   **243**

8. a. 6.3 + 2.9 =   **9.2**   b. 15.7 – 6.1 =   **9.6**

Name: _____ Date: _____

Mental calculation strategies (+ and –)

1 a. 72 – 48 = [_____] b. 104 – 89 = [_____]

2 a. 207 – 186 = [_____] b. 608 – 489 = [_____]

3 a. 2000 – 1952 = [_____] b. 4000 – 2875 = [_____]

4 a. 7000 – 5994 = [_____] b. 8000 – 3996 = [_____]

5 a. 135 + 41 = [_____] b. 261 + 186 = [_____]

6 a. 4206 + 3007 = [_____] b. 5723 + 3992 = [_____]

7 a. 362 – 159 = [_____] b. 541 – 298 = [_____]

8 a. 6.3 + 2.9 = [_____] b. 15.7 – 6.1 = [_____]

Activity sheet questions

Oral

1–10
- Use known number facts and place value to consolidate mental addition/ subtraction (e.g. 470 + 380, 810 – 380, 7.4 + 9.8, 9.2 – 8.6).

Written
- Consolidate all strategies from previous year, including:
- Find a difference by counting up.
  - add or subtract the nearest multiple of 10, 100 or 1000, then adjust

1
  - use the relationship between addition and subtraction

2–4
  - add several numbers.

Teacher note

- Discuss other strategies, e.g. when adding 31, add 30 and then add a further 1, etc. Remind children that the order in which we do addition is unimportant.

Oral questions

1. 560 plus 280.
2. 736 add 250.
3. Increase 2600 by 3200.
4. 3700 plus 2900.
5. 712 minus 307.
6. 6500 subtract 3200.
7. 5300 take away 2900.

What must be added to:

8. 3.85 to make 4?
9. 6.39 to make 7?
10. 5.72 to make 6?

Answers

1.	**840**	6.	**3300**
2.	**986**	7.	**2400**
3.	**5800**	8.	**0.15**
4.	**6600**	9.	**0.61**
5.	**405**	10.	**0.28**

1 Use the +, – and = signs to write as many number sentences as you can with these numbers. 2796, 1584, 4380

2796 + 1584 = 4380	**1584 = 4380 – 2796**
1584 + 2796 = 4380	**2796 – 4380 = –1584**
2796 = 4380 – 1584	**1584 – 4380 = –2796**

2 Add these numbers. a. 9 + 4 + 7 + 1 = **21**   c. 15 + 6 + 5 + 8 + 2 = **36**

b. 12 + 7 + 5 + 8 = **32**   d. 14 + 9 + 5 + 16 + 2 = **46**

3 Find the sum of these numbers. a. 10 + 70 + 90 + 40 = **210**

b. 70 + 80 + 40 + 50 + 20 = **260**

4 Write the totals.

a. 60 + 62 + 67 + 65 = **254**   b. 85 + 83 + 81 + 80 = **329**

Explain how you did these.

e.g. (60 x 4) + (2 + 7 + 5) = 240 + 14 = 254
(80 x 4) + (5 + 3 + 1) = 320 + 9 = 329

Name: _____   Date: _____

ASSESSMENT 12 — Mental calculation strategies (+ and –)

1.	6.
2.	7.
3.	8.
4.	9.
5.	10.

1 Use the +, – and = signs to write as many number sentences as you can with these numbers. 2796, 1584, 4380

2 Add these numbers. a. $9 + 4 + 7 + 1 =$ ☐   c. $15 + 6 + 5 + 8 + 2 =$ ☐

b. $12 + 7 + 5 + 8 =$ ☐   d. $14 + 9 + 5 + 16 + 2 =$ ☐

3 Find the sum of these numbers. a. $10 + 70 + 90 + 40 =$ ☐

b. $70 + 80 + 40 + 50 + 20 =$ ☐

4 Write the totals.

a. $60 + 62 + 67 + 65 =$ ☐   b. $85 + 83 + 81 + 80 =$ ☐

Explain how you did these.

Pencil and paper procedures (+ and -)

Activity sheet questions

Written

1–7
- Use informal pencil and paper methods to support, record or explain additions and subtractions.
  Extend written methods to column addition and subtraction of numbers involving decimals.

Teacher note

- Written methods of addition and subtraction should not be introduced to children until they have a range of sound mental strategies and are confident in ideas of place value for the magnitude of numbers involved in the calculations. Formal written methods of the traditional variety should be built upon informal written methods. Children should always round large numbers and make a mental approximation of the answer before tackling the question. It is important that questions of this type are presented both horizontally and vertically to encourage children to make their own decisions about how to organise the question on paper.

Answers

1
a.
```
  2718
+ 5823
──────
  8541
```
b.
```
  3463
+ 1776
──────
  5239
```
c.
```
  4565
  3209
+ 6171
──────
 13945
```
d.
```
  34072
  69138
+ 78305
───────
 181515
```

2
a.
```
  63581
+ 25372
───────
  88953
```
b.
```
  70963
+ 68978
───────
 139941
```
c.
```
   5418
     57
    805
+    18
───────
   6298
```
d.
```
  89043
    681
   7824
     36
+   109
───────
  97693
```

3 Jo and Jack played the same computer game. Who scored highest, and by how many points?

JO: 65002   JACK: 59381

Jo, by 5621

4
a.
```
  5328
- 4732
──────
   596
```
b.
```
  4808
- 3982
──────
   826
```
c.
```
  29263
- 17626
───────
  11637
```
d.
```
  70032
- 61274
───────
   8758
```

5
a. 5.86m + 9.72m

15.58m

b. 17.73kg + 4.82kg

22.55kg

c. 23.08cm + 17.94cm

41.02cm

6
a.
```
   7.6kg
-  4.9kg
────────
   2.7kg
```
b.
```
   5.78kg
-  2.89kg
─────────
   2.89kg
```
c.
```
  16.0mm
-  8.6mm
────────
   7.4mm
```

7
a. 261.8 – 65.3

196.5

b. 63 – 17.3

45.7

c. 27.38 – 9.2

18.18

Pencil and paper procedures (+ and -)

1
a.
```
  2718
+ 5823
_____
```
b.
```
  3463
+ 1776
_____
```
c.
```
  4565
  3209
+ 6171
_____
```
d.
```
  34072
  69138
+ 78305
_____
```

2
a.
```
  63581
+ 25372
_____
```
b.
```
  70963
+ 68978
_____
```
c.
```
  5418
    57
   805
+   18
_____
```
d.
```
  89043
    681
   7824
     36
+   109
_____
```

3 Jo and Jack played the same computer game.
Who scored highest, and by how many points?

JO: 65002   JACK: 59381

4
a.
```
  5328
- 4732
_____
```
b.
```
  4808
- 3982
_____
```
c.
```
  29263
- 17626
_____
```
d.
```
  70032
- 61274
_____
```

5 a. 5.86m + 9.72m

b. 17.73kg + 4.82kg

c. 23.08cm + 17.94cm

6
a.
```
   7.6kg
- 4.9kg
_____
```
b.
```
   5.78kg
- 2.89kg
_____
```
c.
```
  16.0mm
-  8.6mm
_____
```

7 a. 261.8 – 65.3

b. 63 – 17.3

c. 27.38 – 9.2

Activity sheet questions

Written

1–7 ● Understand and use the relationships between the four operations, and the principles (not the names) of the arithmetic laws.

8–9 Use brackets.

● Express a quotient as a fraction or as a decimal rounded to one decimal place.
Divide £.p by a two-digit number to give £.p.
Round up or down after division, depending on the context.

Teacher note

● Children should appreciate that multiplication and division are repeated addition and subtraction respectively.

● Note the arithmetic laws as they apply to multiplication:
  – **commutative**, i.e. 5 x 3 and 3 x 5 give the same answer
  – **associative**, i.e. the grouping of numbers to be multiplied does not matter,
  e.g. (6 x 4) x 3 = 6 x (4 x 3)
  – **distributive**, i.e. the number to be multiplied can be split into parts and each multiplied separately,
  e.g. 15 x 6 = (10 x 6) + (5 x 6).

● Children should appreciate that these laws can be used to assist in mental multiplication, e.g. it can often be easier to split numbers (distributive law) or to group numbers (associative law) in different ways.

Answers

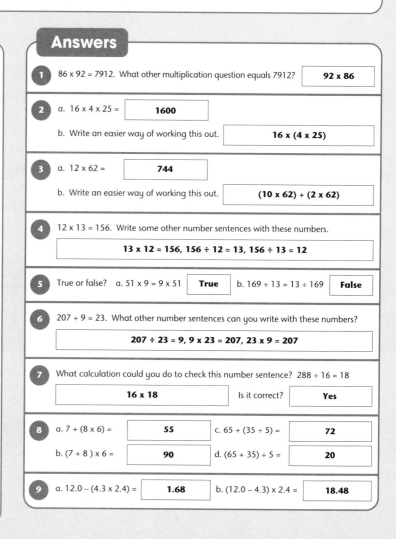

1. 86 x 92 = 7912. What other multiplication question equals 7912? **92 x 86**

2. a. 16 x 4 x 25 = **1600**
b. Write an easier way of working this out. **16 x (4 x 25)**

3. a. 12 x 62 = **744**
b. Write an easier way of working this out. **(10 x 62) + (2 x 62)**

4. 12 x 13 = 156. Write some other number sentences with these numbers.
13 x 12 = 156, 156 ÷ 12 = 13, 156 ÷ 13 = 12

5. True or false? a. 51 x 9 = 9 x 51 **True** b. 169 ÷ 13 = 13 ÷ 169 **False**

6. 207 ÷ 9 = 23. What other number sentences can you write with these numbers?
207 ÷ 23 = 9, 9 x 23 = 207, 23 x 9 = 207

7. What calculation could you do to check this number sentence? 288 ÷ 16 = 18
16 x 18 Is it correct? **Yes**

8. a. 7 + (8 x 6) = **55** c. 65 + (35 ÷ 5) = **72**
b. (7 + 8) x 6 = **90** d. (65 + 35) ÷ 5 = **20**

9. a. 12.0 – (4.3 x 2.4) = **1.68** b. (12.0 – 4.3) x 2.4 = **18.48**

Name: _____   Date: _____

1   86 x 92 = 7912. What other multiplication question equals 7912?   [ ]

2   a.   16 x 4 x 25 = [ ]

      b.   Write an easier way of working this out. [ ]

3   a.   12 x 62 = [ ]

      b.   Write an easier way of working this out. [ ]

4   12 x 13 = 156. Write some other number sentences with these numbers.

[ ]

5   True or false?   a. 51 x 9 = 9 x 51   [ ]   b. 169 ÷ 13 = 13 ÷ 169   [ ]

6   207 ÷ 9 = 23. What other number sentences can you write with these numbers?

[ ]

7   What calculation could you do to check this number sentence? 288 ÷ 16 = 18

[ ]   Is it correct? [ ]

8   a. 7 + (8 x 6) = [ ]   c. 65 + (35 ÷ 5) = [ ]

      b. (7 + 8) x 6 = [ ]   d. (65 + 35) ÷ 5 = [ ]

9   a. 12.0 – (4.3 x 2.4) = [ ]   b. (12.0 – 4.3) x 2.4 = [ ]

Activity sheet questions

Oral

1–10 ● Understand and use the relationships between the four operations, and the principles (not the names) of the arithmetic laws.
Use brackets.

Written

1–3 ● Express a quotient as a fraction or as a decimal rounded to one decimal place.
4 Divide £.p by a two-digit number to give £.p.
5–6 Round up or down after division, depending on the context.

Teacher note

● The 'quotient' is the result of dividing one number by another, e.g. if 8 is divided by 4 the quotient is 2.
● Children should be encouraged to check the reasonableness of their answers in the context of the question.

Answers

1. **130**	6. **11**
2. **600**	7. **16**
3. **0**	8. **19**
4. **72**	9. **4**
5. **0.9**	10. **(e.g. 3 ÷ 2, 6 ÷ 4, 12 ÷ 8)**

1 Give any remainder as a fraction.

a. $86 \div 8 =$ $\boxed{10\frac{6}{8} \text{ (or } 10\frac{3}{4})}$ b. $93 \div 7 =$ $\boxed{13\frac{2}{7}}$

2 Write any remainder as a decimal.

a. $628 \div 8 =$ $\boxed{78.5}$ b. $417 \div 100 =$ $\boxed{4.17}$

3 Write your answer to one decimal place.

a. $128 \div 7 =$ $\boxed{18.2}$ b. $137 \div 6 =$ $\boxed{22.8}$

4 It cost a group of 13 people a total of £55.25 to get into the cinema. How much did each person pay? $\boxed{£4.25}$

5 Cath wants some strips of ribbon that are 32cm in length. How many can she get from a length of 4m? $\boxed{12}$

6 586 apples have been delivered to the grocer's. Each box holds 36 apples. How many boxes were needed for the delivery? $\boxed{17}$

Oral questions

1. Double 65.
2. What is the product of 150 and 4?
3. Multiply 25 by 8 by 0.
4. 9 times 8 equals what?
5. What number times 5 equals 4.5?
6. Divide 99 by 9.
7. If you shared 112 sweets equally between 7 people, how many sweets would each person get?
8. How many lengths of 25cm can you cut from 475cm?
9. What is the remainder when 116 is divided by 8?
10. Think of two numbers with a quotient of 1.5.

Name: _____ Date: _____

1.	6.
2.	7.
3.	8.
4.	9.
5.	10.

1 Give any remainder as a fraction.

a. 86 ÷ 8 = [ ]   b. 93 ÷ 7 = [ ]

2 Write any remainder as a decimal.

a. 628 ÷ 8 = [ ]   b. 417 ÷ 100 = [ ]

3 Write your answer to one decimal place.

a. 128 ÷ 7 = [ ]   b. 137 ÷ 6 = [ ]

4 It cost a group of 13 people a total of £55.25 to get into the cinema. How much did each person pay? [ ]

5 Cath wants some strips of ribbon that are 32cm in length. How many can she get from a length of 4m? [ ]

6 586 apples have been delivered to the grocer's. Each box holds 36 apples. How many boxes were needed for the delivery? [ ]

Mental calculation strategies (x and ÷)

Activity sheet questions

Written

1–9
- Use related facts and doubling or halving. For example:
  - double or halve the most significant digit first
  - to multiply by 25, multiply by 100 then divide by 4
  - double one number and halve the other
  - find the x24 table by doubling the x6 table twice.

10
- Use factors (e.g. 35 x 18 = 35 x 6 x 3).
  - Use closely related facts: for example, multiply by 49 or 51 by multiplying by 50 and adjusting.
    Develop the x17 table by adding facts from the x10 and x7 tables.
  - Partition (e.g. 87 x 6 = (80 x 6) + (7 x 6); 3.4 x 3 = (3 x 3) + (0.4 x 3)).
  - Use the relationship between multiplication and division.
  - Use known number facts and place value to consolidate mental multiplication and division.

Teacher note

- Encourage children to modify and adapt strategies already known to create new ones, such as x100 ÷ 4 to create x25. Invite them to verbalise their strategies at all times and to make jottings to explain their ideas to others.

Answers

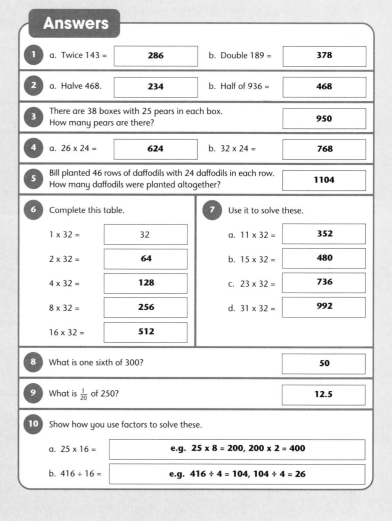

1   a. Twice 143 = **286**   b. Double 189 = **378**

2   a. Halve 468. **234**   b. Half of 936 = **468**

3   There are 38 boxes with 25 pears in each box. How many pears are there? **950**

4   a. 26 x 24 = **624**   b. 32 x 24 = **768**

5   Bill planted 46 rows of daffodils with 24 daffodils in each row. How many daffodils were planted altogether? **1104**

6   Complete this table.

1 x 32 =	32
2 x 32 =	64
4 x 32 =	128
8 x 32 =	256
16 x 32 =	512

7   Use it to solve these.

a. 11 x 32 =	352
b. 15 x 32 =	480
c. 23 x 32 =	736
d. 31 x 32 =	992

8   What is one sixth of 300? **50**

9   What is $\frac{1}{20}$ of 250? **12.5**

10   Show how you use factors to solve these.

a. 25 x 16 =   **e.g. 25 x 8 = 200, 200 x 2 = 400**

b. 416 ÷ 16 =   **e.g. 416 ÷ 4 = 104, 104 ÷ 4 = 26**

Name: _____   Date: _____

1   a. Twice 143 = [   ]   b. Double 189 = [   ]

2   a. Halve 468. [   ]   b. Half of 936 = [   ]

3   There are 38 boxes with 25 pears in each box.
How many pears are there?   [   ]

4   a. 26 x 24 = [   ]   b. 32 x 24 = [   ]

5   Bill planted 46 rows of daffodils with 24 daffodils in each row.
How many daffodils were planted altogether?   [   ]

6   Complete this table.

1 x 32 = [32   ]

2 x 32 = [   ]

4 x 32 = [   ]

8 x 32 = [   ]

16 x 32 = [   ]

7   Use it to solve these.

a. 11 x 32 = [   ]

b. 15 x 32 = [   ]

c. 23 x 32 = [   ]

d. 31 x 32 = [   ]

8   What is one sixth of 300?   [   ]

9   What is $\frac{1}{20}$ of 250?   [   ]

10   Show how you use factors to solve these.

a. 25 x 16 = [   ]

b. 416 ÷ 16 = [   ]

Activity sheet questions

- Use related facts and doubling or halving. For example:
  - double or halve the most significant digit first
  - to multiply by 25, multiply by 100 then divide by 4
  - double one number and halve the other
  - find the x24 table by doubling the x6 table twice.
- Use factors (e.g. 35 x 18 = 35 x 6 x 3).

Oral

1–10 ● Use known number facts and place value to consolidate mental multiplication and division.

Written

1 Develop the x17 table by adding facts from the x10 and x7 tables.

2–4 ● Use closely related facts: for example, multiply by 49 or 51 by multiplying by 50 and adjusting.

5 ● Partition (e.g. 87 x 6 = (80 x 6) + (7 x 6); 3.4 x 3 = (3 x 3) + (0.4 x 3)).

6–7 ● Use the relationship between multiplication and division.

Teacher note

- Encourage children to modify and adapt strategies already known to create new ones. Invite them to verbalise their strategies at all times and to make jottings.

Oral questions

1. 2.38 multiplied by 10.
2. 6.3 times 100.
3. 57 divided by 10.
4. 38 divided by 100.
5. Divide 100 by 7.
6. Double 0.8.
7. Halve 0.35.
8. 0.6 lots of 7 equals?
9. What times 6 equals 1.8?
10. What is the product of 46 and 7?

Answers

1. **23.8**		6. **1.6**	
2. **630**		7. **0.175**	
3. **5.7**		8. **4.2**	
4. **0.38**		9. **0.3**	
5. **0.07**		10. **322**	

1   a. 17 x 24 = **408**   b. 17 x 32 = **544**

2   a. 15 x 19 = **285**   b. 26 x 49 = **1274**

3   a. 16 x 21 = **336**   b. 51 x 25 = **1275**

4   a. 12 x 99 = **1188**   b. 23 x 101 = **2323**

5   a. 74 x 6 = **444**   b. 5.2 x 7 = **36.4**

6   1.25 x 8 = 10   What other number sentences can you write with these numbers?

8 x 1.25 = 10   **10 ÷ 8 = 1.25**   **10 ÷ 1.25 = 8**

7   Use the numbers 0.4, 0.3 and 0.12 to write four multiplication or division sentences.

0.4 x 0.3 = 0.12   **0.3 x 0.4 = 0.12**

0.12 ÷ 0.4 = 0.3   **0.12 ÷ 0.3 = 0.4**

Name: _____ Date: _____

1.	6.
2.	7.
3.	8.
4.	9.
5.	10.

1 a. 17 x 24 = [ ] b. 17 x 32 = [ ]

2 a. 15 x 19 = [ ] b. 26 x 49 = [ ]

3 a. 16 x 21 = [ ] b. 51 x 25 = [ ]

4 a. 12 x 99 = [ ] b. 23 x 101 = [ ]

5 a. 74 x 6 = [ ] b. 5.2 x 7 = [ ]

6 1.25 x 8 = 10 What other number sentences can you write with these numbers?

7 Use the numbers 0.4, 0.3 and 0.12 to write four multiplication or division sentences.

Pencil and paper procedures (x and ÷)

Activity sheet questions

Written

- Approximate first. Use informal pencil and paper methods to support, record or explain multiplications and divisions.
  Extend written methods to:

1–3
- multiplication of ThHTU x U (short multiplication)

4–6
- short multiplication of numbers involving decimals

7–8
- long multiplication of a three-digit by a two-digit integer
- short division of TU or HTU by U (mixed-number answer)
- division of HTU by TU (long division, whole-number answer)
- short division of numbers involving decimals.

Teacher note

- Children should always round large numbers and make a mental approximation of the answer before tackling the question. Written methods of multiplication and division should not be introduced to children until they have a range of sound mental strategies and are confident in ideas of place value for the magnitude of numbers involved in the calculations. Formal written methods of the traditional variety should be built upon informal written methods.

- It is important that questions of this type are presented both horizontally and vertically to encourage children to make their own decisions about how to organise the question on paper.

Answers

Approximate first, then find the answers to these questions.
Use the space for your working out.

1. $1863 \times 7 =$ **13 041**

2. 2423 rows with 8 plants per row.
   How many plants?   **19 384**

3. $3524 \times 7 =$ **24 668**

4. $8.27 \times 6 =$ **49.62**

5. 5.69 litres of oil at £3 a litre costs?   £ **17.07**

6. $2.84 \times 7 =$ **19.88**

7. $352 \times 35 =$ **12 320**

8. $509 \times 47 =$ **23 923**

Name: _____   Date: _____

Approximate first, then find the answers to these questions.
Use the space for your working out.

1   1863 x 7 = [   ]

2   2423 rows with 8 plants per row.
How many plants?

[   ]

3   3524 x 7 = [   ]

4   8.27 x 6 = [   ]

5   5.69 litres of oil at £3 a litre costs?

£ [   ]

6   2.84 x 7 = [   ]

7   352 x 35 = [   ]

8   509 x 47 = [   ]

Activity sheet questions

Written

● Approximate first. Use informal pencil and paper methods to support, record or explain multiplications and divisions.
Extend written methods to:

1–3 – short division of TU or HTU by U (mixed-number answer)
4–7 – division of HTU by TU (long division, whole-number answer)
8–10 – short division of numbers involving decimals.
– multiplication of ThHTU x U (short multiplication)
– short multiplication of numbers involving decimals
– long multiplication of a three-digit by a two-digit integer.

Teacher note

● Children should always round large numbers and make a mental approximation of the answer before tackling the question. Written methods of multiplication and division should not be introduced to children until they have a range of sound mental strategies and are confident in ideas of place value for the magnitude of numbers involved in the calculations. Formal written methods of the traditional variety should be built upon informal written methods.

● It is important that questions of this type are presented both horizontally and vertically to encourage children to make their own decisions about how to organise the question on paper.

Answers

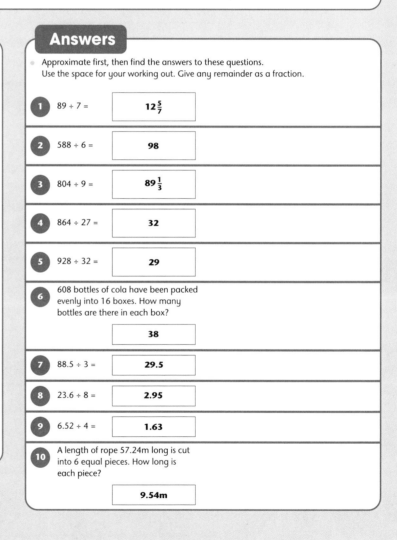

Approximate first, then find the answers to these questions.
Use the space for your working out. Give any remainder as a fraction.

1 $89 \div 7 =$ $12\frac{5}{7}$

2 $588 \div 6 =$ 98

3 $804 \div 9 =$ $89\frac{1}{3}$

4 $864 \div 27 =$ 32

5 $928 \div 32 =$ 29

6 608 bottles of cola have been packed evenly into 16 boxes. How many bottles are there in each box?
    38

7 $88.5 \div 3 =$ 29.5

8 $23.6 \div 8 =$ 2.95

9 $6.52 \div 4 =$ 1.63

10 A length of rope 57.24m long is cut into 6 equal pieces. How long is each piece?
    $9.54m$

Name: _____   Date: _____

● Approximate first, then find the answers to these questions.
Use the space for your working out. Give any remainder as a fraction.

1 89 ÷ 7 =

2 588 ÷ 6 =

3 804 ÷ 9 =

4 864 ÷ 27 =

5 928 ÷ 32 =

6 608 bottles of cola have been packed evenly into 16 boxes. How many bottles are there in each box?

7 88.5 ÷ 3 =

8 23.6 ÷ 8 =

9 6.52 ÷ 4 =

10 A length of rope 57.24m long is cut into 6 equal pieces. How long is each piece?

Activity sheet questions

Written

1–5

● **Solve mathematical problems or puzzles, recognise and explain patterns and relationships, generalise and predict.**

Suggest extensions asking 'What if … ?'

● Make and investigate a general statement about familiar numbers or shapes by finding examples that satisfy it.

Develop from explaining a generalised relationship in words to expressing it in a formula using letters as symbols (e.g. the cost of n articles at 15p each).

Teacher note

● Children need to develop a wide range of vocabulary when exploring patterns and making generalisations of this type. Words in this assessment include 'statement', 'sequence', 'term' and 'formula'.

● Children should be encouraged to tackle problems and puzzles systematically and develop skills of problem-solving and investigation, such as simplifying, visualising, using trial and error, and generalising. In order to do so, they will need experience of a wide variety of situations which require these skills.

Answers

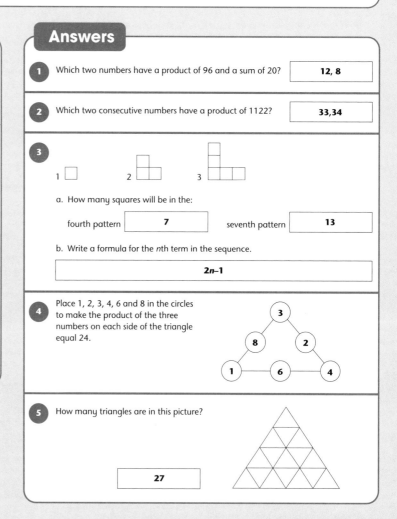

1 Which two numbers have a product of 96 and a sum of 20? **12, 8**

2 Which two consecutive numbers have a product of 1122? **33, 34**

3

1   2   3

a. How many squares will be in the:

fourth pattern **7**   seventh pattern **13**

b. Write a formula for the nth term in the sequence.

$2n-1$

4 Place 1, 2, 3, 4, 6 and 8 in the circles to make the product of the three numbers on each side of the triangle equal 24.

3
8   2
1   6   4

5 How many triangles are in this picture?

27

Name: _____   Date: _____

1   Which two numbers have a product of 96 and a sum of 20?   [   ]

2   Which two consecutive numbers have a product of 1122?   [   ]

3

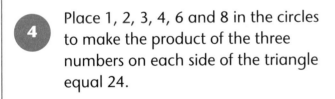

1   2   3

a.   How many squares will be in the:

fourth pattern [   ]   seventh pattern [   ]

b.   Write a formula for the *n*th term in the sequence.

[   ]

4   Place 1, 2, 3, 4, 6 and 8 in the circles to make the product of the three numbers on each side of the triangle equal 24.

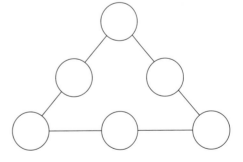

5   How many triangles are in this picture?

[   ]

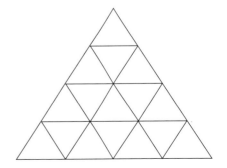

21 Reasoning and generalising about numbers or shapes

Activity sheet questions

Written

1 • Solve mathematical problems or puzzles, recognise and explain patterns and relationships, generalise and predict.
Suggest extensions asking 'What of … ?'

2–6 • Make and investigate a general statement about familiar numbers or shapes by finding examples that satisfy it.
Develop from explaining a generalised relationship in words to expressing it in a formula using letters as symbols (e.g. the cost of *n* articles at 15p each).

Teacher note

• Children need to develop a wide range of vocabulary when exploring patterns and making generalisations of this type. Words in this test include 'statement', 'sequence', 'term' and 'formula'.

• Children should be encouraged to tackle problems and puzzles systematically and develop skills of problem-solving and investigation, such as simplifying, visualising, using trial and error, and generalising. In order to do so, they will need experience of a wide variety of situations which require these skills.

Answers

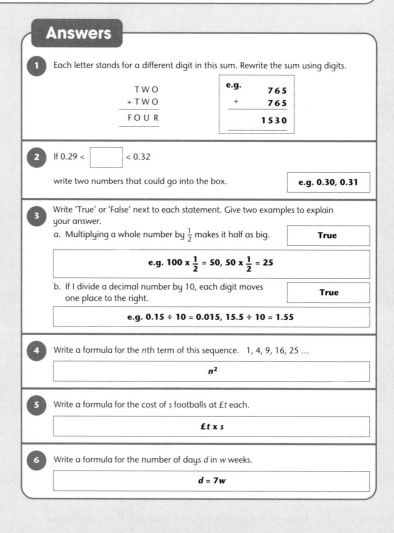

1 Each letter stands for a different digit in this sum. Rewrite the sum using digits.

```
  T W O          e.g.      7 6 5
+ T W O          +         7 6 5
---------                --------
F O U R                  1 5 3 0
```

2 If $0.29 <$ ☐ < 0.32

write two numbers that could go into the box.   **e.g. 0.30, 0.31**

3 Write 'True' or 'False' next to each statement. Give two examples to explain your answer.
a. Multiplying a whole number by $\frac{1}{2}$ makes it half as big.   **True**

e.g. $100 \times \frac{1}{2} = 50$, $50 \times \frac{1}{2} = 25$

b. If I divide a decimal number by 10, each digit moves one place to the right.   **True**

e.g. $0.15 \div 10 = 0.015$, $15.5 \div 10 = 1.55$

4 Write a formula for the *n*th term of this sequence.   1, 4, 9, 16, 25 …

n^2

5 Write a formula for the cost of *s* footballs at £*t* each.

£*t* x *s*

6 Write a formula for the number of days *d* in *w* weeks.

$d = 7w$

Name: _____ Date: _____

 Reasoning and generalising about numbers or shapes

1 Each letter stands for a different digit in this sum. Rewrite the sum using digits.

$$
\begin{array}{r}
T\,W\,O \\
+\,T\,W\,O \\
\hline
F\,O\,U\,R
\end{array}
$$

2 If $0.29 < \boxed{} < 0.32$

write two numbers that could go into the box.

3 Write 'True' or 'False' next to each statement. Give two examples to explain your answer.

a. Multiplying a whole number by $\frac{1}{2}$ makes it half as big.

b. If I divide a decimal number by 10, each digit moves one place to the right.

4 Write a formula for the nth term of this sequence.   1, 4, 9, 16, 25 …

5 Write a formula for the cost of s footballs at £t each.

6 Write a formula for the number of days d in w weeks.

© Folens (copiable page)

22 Problems involving 'real life', money or measures

Activity sheet questions

Written

1-7
- Identify and use appropriate operations (including combinations of operations) to solve word problems involving numbers and quantities based on 'real life', money or measures (including time), using one or more steps, including converting pounds to foreign currency, or vice versa, and calculating percentages such as VAT.

Explain methods and reasoning.

Teacher note

- When worded questions are introduced to children, ensure that a range of operations is required. Children can sometimes fall into the pattern that these are 'all addition' and avoid thinking about the context at all. Children should be encouraged to focus on the important parts of the question, ignoring any information that may be superfluous.
- Maximise real-life opportunities that present themselves in the classroom, such as calculating dinner money for the class, the school, etc.
- Calculators are particularly useful in problem-solving situations as they enable children both to maintain attention on the problem and to use realistically large numbers.

Answers

1. A football team scored 96 goals in 40 games. What is the mean number of goals per game? — **2.4**

2. The garden centre has 27 rows of roses. There are 32 roses in each row.
   a. How many roses are there in total? — **864**
   b. How many rows would be needed for 544 roses? — **17**

3. 8567 metres of string were sold last year by a local DIY shop. How many more did it need to sell to have sold 10 000 metres? — **1433m**

4. A litre of cola costs 78p. How much would it cost to fill five 6-litre jugs? — **£23.40**

5. What change do you get from £50 if you buy six T shirts at £7.35 each? — **£5.90**

6. A record store has 14 shelves of 25 CDs on each of four walls. How many CDs are there in the store? — **1400**

7. These prices have been halved in a sale. Write the new price for each item.

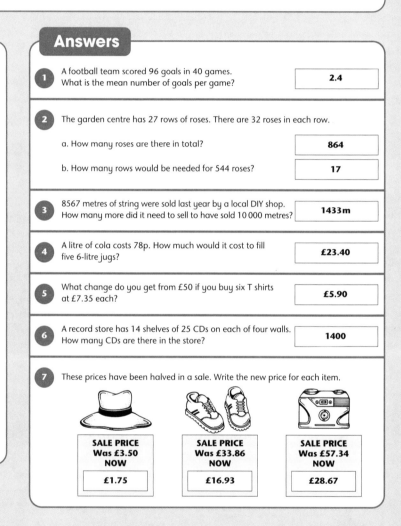

SALE PRICE
Was £3.50
NOW
£1.75

SALE PRICE
Was £33.86
NOW
£16.93

SALE PRICE
Was £57.34
NOW
£28.67

Name: _____ Date: _____

1 A football team scored 96 goals in 40 games.
What is the mean number of goals per game?

2 The garden centre has 27 rows of roses. There are 32 roses in each row.

a. How many roses are there in total?

b. How many rows would be needed for 544 roses?

3 8567 metres of string were sold last year by a local DIY shop.
How many more did it need to sell to have sold 10 000 metres?

4 A litre of cola costs 78p. How much would it cost to fill
five 6-litre jugs?

5 What change do you get from £50 if you buy six T shirts
at £7.35 each?

6 A record store has 14 shelves of 25 CDs on each of four walls.
How many CDs are there in the store?

7 These prices have been halved in a sale. Write the new price for each item.

SALE PRICE Was £3.50 NOW	SALE PRICE Was £33.86 NOW	SALE PRICE Was £57.34 NOW
£	£	£

Activity sheet questions

Written

1–5
- Identify and use appropriate operations (including combinations of operations) to solve word problems involving numbers and quantities based on 'real life', money or measures (including time), using one or more steps, including converting pounds to foreign currency, or vice versa, and calculating percentages such as VAT.

  Explain methods and reasoning.

Teacher note

- When worded questions are introduced to children, ensure that a range of operations is required. Children can sometimes fall into the pattern that these are 'all addition' and avoid thinking about the context at all. Children should be encouraged to focus on the important parts of the question, ignoring any information that may be superfluous.
- Maximise real-life opportunities that present themselves in the classroom, such as calculating dinner money for the class, the school, etc.
- Calculators are particularly useful in problem-solving situations as they enable children both to maintain attention on the problem and to use realistically large numbers.

Answers

1 I have a journey of 1060 kilometres. If I drove 280 kilometres before lunch and 203 kilometres after lunch, how much further do I have to go to have driven:

a. halfway?

47 kilometres

b. two thirds of the way?

706 kilometres

c. What fraction of the journey is 424 kilometres?

$\frac{2}{5}$

2 Exchange rates for £1 are: 1.6 US dollars, 425 Greek drachmas, 1.3 euros.

a. How many of each of these currencies would you get for £50?

US dollars	drachmas	euros
80	**21 250**	**65**

b. How many £s would you get for:

16 US dollars? **£10**   160 US dollars? **£100**

c. How many euros would you get for:

1.6 US dollars? **1.3 euros**   4.8 US dollars? **3.9 euros**

d. What would be the price in £s of a TV costing 1300 euros? **£1000**

3 A film on television started at 18:55 and ended at 21:16. There was a 20-minute break for the news. How long was the film? **2 hours, 1 minute**

4 A coach travelling at a constant speed leaves at 11:15 and arrives at 13:45. What time is it when the coach has travelled:

a. one tenth of the journey? **11.30**   b. four fifths of the journey? **13.15**

5 VAT is charged at 17.5%. Work out the VAT on these items and add it to find the total cost.

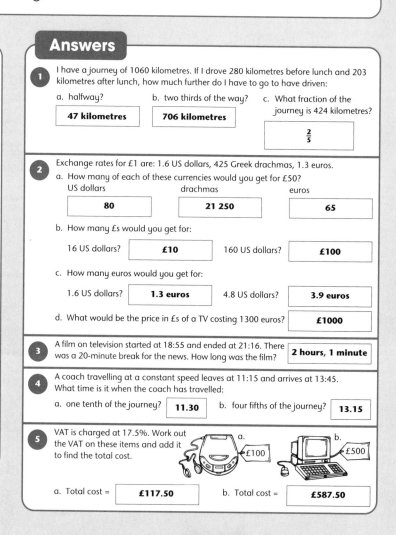

a. £100   b. £500

a. Total cost = **£117.50**   b. Total cost = **£587.50**

23 **Problems involving 'real life', money or measures**

1 I have a journey of 1060 kilometres. If I drove 280 kilometres before lunch and 203 kilometres after lunch, how much further do I have to go to have driven:

a. halfway?

b. two thirds of the way?

c. What fraction of the journey is 424 kilometres?

2 Exchange rates for £1 are: 1.6 US dollars, 425 Greek drachmas, 1.3 euros.

a. How many of each of these currencies would you get for £50?

US dollars   drachmas   euros

b. How many £s would you get for:

16 US dollars?   160 US dollars?

c. How many euros would you get for:

1.6 US dollars?   4.8 US dollars?

d. What would be the price in £s of a TV costing 1300 euros?

3 A film on television started at 18:55 and ended at 21:16. There was a 20-minute break for the news. How long was the film?

4 A coach travelling at a constant speed leaves at 11:15 and arrives at 13:45. What time is it when the coach has travelled:

a. one tenth of the journey?   b. four fifths of the journey?

5 VAT is charged at 17.5%. Work out the VAT on these items and add it to find the total cost.

a.

£100

b.

£500

a. Total cost =   b. Total cost =

Activity sheet questions

Written
1–6

- Solve a problem by representing, extracting and interpreting data in tables, graphs, charts and diagrams, including those generated by a computer, for example: line graphs (e.g. for distance/time, for a multiplication table, a conversion graph, a graph of pairs of numbers adding to 8); frequency tables and bar charts with grouped discrete data (e.g. test marks 0–5, 6–10, 11–15 …).
- Use the language associated with probability to discuss events, including those with equally likely outcomes.
- Find the mode and range of a set of data.
  Begin to find the median and mean of a set of data.

Teacher note

- Encourage children to see the purpose of grouping data in class intervals, as shown in the first question. If each throw were recorded precisely, e.g. 22.5m, and drawn in a separate column on the bar chart, it would be virtually impossible to draw conclusions from the graph. By using class intervals, generalisations can be made, such as most children threw between 30m and 39m.

Answers

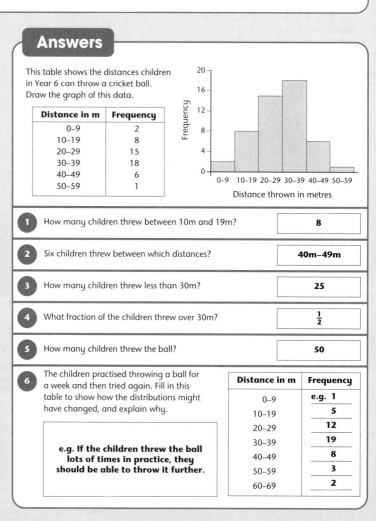

This table shows the distances children in Year 6 can throw a cricket ball. Draw the graph of this data.

Distance in m	Frequency
0–9	2
10–19	8
20–29	15
30–39	18
40–49	6
50–59	1

1 How many children threw between 10m and 19m? **8**

2 Six children threw between which distances? **40m–49m**

3 How many children threw less than 30m? **25**

4 What fraction of the children threw over 30m? $\frac{1}{2}$

5 How many children threw the ball? **50**

6 The children practised throwing a ball for a week and then tried again. Fill in this table to show how the distributions might have changed, and explain why.

e.g. If the children threw the ball lots of times in practice, they should be able to throw it further.

Distance in m	Frequency
0–9	e.g. 1
10–19	5
20–29	12
30–39	19
40–49	8
50–59	3
60–69	2

Name: _____   Date: _____

Handling data

This table shows the distances children in Year 6 can throw a cricket ball. Draw the graph of this data.

Distance in m	Frequency
0–9	2
10–19	8
20–29	15
30–39	18
40–49	6
50–59	1

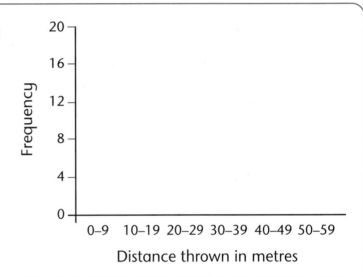

Distance thrown in metres

---

1 How many children threw between 10m and 19m?

---

2 Six children threw between which distances?

---

3 How many children threw less than 30m?

---

4 What fraction of the children threw over 30m?

---

5 How many children threw the ball?

---

6 The children practised throwing a ball for a week and then tried again. Fill in this table to show how the distributions might have changed, and explain why.

Distance in m	Frequency
0–9	_____
10–19	_____
20–29	_____
30–39	_____
40–49	_____
50–59	_____
60–69	_____

Handling data

Activity sheet questions

Written

1–7
- Solve a problem by representing, extracting and interpreting data in tables, graphs, charts and diagrams, including those generated by a computer, for example: line graphs (e.g. for distance/time, for a multiplication table, a conversion graph, a graph of pairs of numbers adding to 8); frequency tables and bar charts with grouped discrete data (e.g. test marks 0–5, 6–10, 11–15 …).
- Use the language associated with probability to discuss events, including those with equally likely outcomes.
- Find the mode and range of a set of data.
  Begin to find the median and mean of a set of data.

Teacher note

- Children need experiences of estimating fractions of a circle in order to draw conclusions from a pie chart. If children find this difficult, encourage them to draw marks around the pie chart to divide it equally into parts, and then to count the parts making up each region. For example, if the circle is split into 12 parts, approximately 5 might be 'football', producing the fraction $\frac{5}{12}$.

Answers

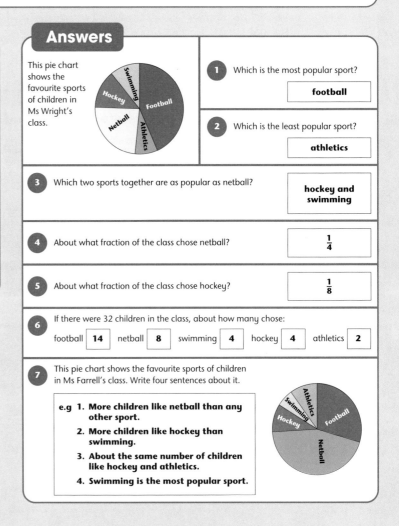

This pie chart shows the favourite sports of children in Ms Wright's class.

1. Which is the most popular sport?

   football

2. Which is the least popular sport?

   athletics

3. Which two sports together are as popular as netball?

   hockey and swimming

4. About what fraction of the class chose netball?

   $\frac{1}{4}$

5. About what fraction of the class chose hockey?

   $\frac{1}{8}$

6. If there were 32 children in the class, about how many chose:

   football **14**   netball **8**   swimming **4**   hockey **4**   athletics **2**

7. This pie chart shows the favourite sports of children in Ms Farrell's class. Write four sentences about it.

   e.g
   1. **More children like netball than any other sport.**
   2. **More children like hockey than swimming.**
   3. **About the same number of children like hockey and athletics.**
   4. **Swimming is the most popular sport.**

Name: _____ Date: _____

This pie chart shows the favourite sports of children in Ms Wright's class.

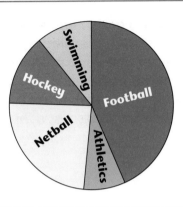

1 Which is the most popular sport?

2 Which is the least popular sport?

3 Which two sports together are as popular as netball?

4 About what fraction of the class chose netball?

5 About what fraction of the class chose hockey?

6 If there were 32 children in the class, about how many chose:

football [ ] netball [ ] swimming [ ] hockey [ ] athletics [ ]

7 This pie chart shows the favourite sports of children in Ms Farrell's class. Write four sentences about it.

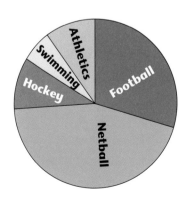

Activity sheet questions

Written

1–3

- Solve a problem by representing, extracting and interpreting data in tables, graphs, charts and diagrams, including those generated by a computer, for example: line graphs (e.g. for distance/time, for a multiplication table, a conversion graph, a graph of pairs of numbers adding to 8); frequency tables and bar charts with grouped discrete data (e.g. test marks 0–5, 6–10, 11–15 …).
- Use the language associated with probability to discuss events, including those with equally likely outcomes.
- Find the mode and range of a set of data.
  Begin to find the median and mean of a set of data.

Teacher note

- When using conversion graphs it is often easier for children to draw horizontal and vertical lines to read the graph accurately. Encourage them to see that a conversion graph enables you to convert any number on one scale to the other, and vice versa. When drawing their own conversion graphs, remind them to plot more than three points on the graph to ensure that the straight line drawn is correct.

Answers

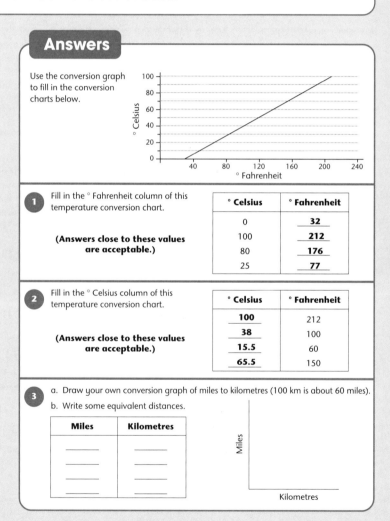

Use the conversion graph to fill in the conversion charts below.

1 Fill in the ° Fahrenheit column of this temperature conversion chart.

(Answers close to these values are acceptable.)

° Celsius	° Fahrenheit
0	**32**
100	**212**
80	**176**
25	**77**

2 Fill in the ° Celsius column of this temperature conversion chart.

(Answers close to these values are acceptable.)

° Celsius	° Fahrenheit
100	212
38	100
15.5	60
65.5	150

3 a. Draw your own conversion graph of miles to kilometres (100 km is about 60 miles).

b. Write some equivalent distances.

Miles	Kilometres
___	___
___	___
___	___
___	___

Handling data

Use the conversion graph to fill in the conversion charts below.

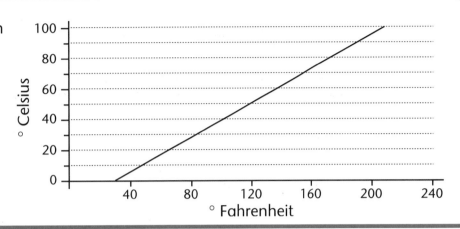

° Fahrenheit

1 Fill in the ° Fahrenheit column of this temperature conversion chart.

° Celsius	° Fahrenheit
0	_____
100	_____
80	_____
25	_____

2 Fill in the ° Celsius column of this temperature conversion chart.

° Celsius	° Fahrenheit
_____	212
_____	100
_____	60
_____	150

3 a. Draw your own conversion graph of miles to kilometres (100 km is about 60 miles).

b. Write some equivalent distances.

Miles	Kilometres
_____	_____
_____	_____
_____	_____
_____	_____

Miles

Kilometres

Activity sheet questions

Oral 1–10 &
Written 1
- Use the language associated with probability to discuss events, including those with equally likely outcomes.

Written 2–5
- Find the mode and range of a set of data.
  Begin to find the median and mean of a set of data.
  - Solve a problem by representing, extracting and interpreting data in tables, graphs, charts and diagrams, including those generated by a computer, for example: line graphs (e.g. for distance/time, for a multiplication table, a conversion graph, a graph of pairs of numbers adding to 8); frequency tables and bar charts with grouped discrete data (e.g. test marks 0–5, 6–10, 11–15 …).

Teacher note

- In a set of data, the 'mode' is the value that occurs most often. There can be more than one mode, as in 6, 7, 7, 7, 8, 9, 9, 9, 10 (7 and 9). The 'range' is the difference between the highest and lowest value.
- The 'median' is the middle number in a sequence of numbers arranged in ascending order, and the 'mean' is calculated by adding n numbers together and dividing their sum by n.

Oral questions

Begin the test by saying, 'Write the probability for each of these statements'.

1. getting heads when you toss a coin
2. throwing an odd number on a dice
3. throwing a 6 on a standard dice
4. throwing a 0 on a standard dice
5. throwing a number less than 5
6. throwing a multiple of 2
7. throwing a number greater than 4
8. getting a red card when you pick from a pack of cards
9. getting a diamond when you pick from a pack of cards
10. getting an ace when you pick from a pack of cards.

Answers

1. $\frac{1}{2}$		6. $\frac{1}{2}$	
2. $\frac{1}{2}$		7. $\frac{2}{6}$	
3. $\frac{1}{6}$		8. $\frac{1}{2}$	
4. 0		9. $\frac{1}{4}$	
5. $\frac{4}{6}$		10. $\frac{1}{13}$	

1 Write an example for the probability shown.

$$0 \qquad \frac{1}{4} \qquad \frac{1}{2} \qquad \frac{5}{6} \qquad 1$$

e.g. Picking a club from a pack of cards	e.g. Tossing a coin to get a head	e.g. Rolling a number less than 6 on a dice

2 Write the mode and range of this list of numbers. 8, 6, 5, 6, 1, 9, 5, 4, 6, 1

a. Mode **6** b. Range **8**

3 Write the median of these lists of numbers.

a. 1, 2, 2, 3, 5, 7, 8, 9, 14 **5** b. 12, 9, 13, 17, 8, 5, 16, 14 **12.5**

4 These are the scores of a hockey team in 7 matches: 6, 1, 1, 3, 5, 8, 4. Find the mean. **4**

5 In question 4, what is the:

a. range of the numbers? **7**
b. mode? **1**
c. median? **4**

Name: _____ Date: _____

1.	6.
2.	7.
3.	8.
4.	9.
5.	10.

1 Write an example for the probability shown.

$0 \qquad \frac{1}{4} \qquad \frac{1}{2} \qquad \frac{5}{6} \qquad 1$

2 Write the mode and range of this list of numbers. 8, 6, 5, 6, 1, 9, 5, 4, 6, 1

a. Mode [   ]   b. Range [   ]

3 Write the median of these lists of numbers.

a. 1, 2, 2, 3, 5, 7, 8, 9, 14 [   ]   b. 12, 9, 13, 17, 8, 5, 16, 14 [   ]

4 These are the scores of a hockey team in 7 matches:
6, 1, 1, 3, 5, 8, 4. Find the mean. [   ]

5 In question 4, what is the: b. mode? [   ]

a. range of the numbers? [   ]   c. median? [   ]

ASSESSMENT
28

Activity sheet questions

Oral

1-10
- Use, read and write standard metric units (km, m, cm, mm, kg, g, l, ml, cl), including their abbreviations, and relationships between them.
  Convert smaller to larger units (e.g. m to km, cm or mm to m, g to kg, ml to l) and vice versa.
  Know imperial units (mile, pint, gallon, lb, oz).
  Know rough equivalents of lb and kg, oz and g, miles and km, litres and pints or gallons.

Written

1-2, 4
- Suggest suitable units and measuring equipment to estimate or measure length, mass or capacity.

3
  Record estimates and readings from scales to a suitable degree of accuracy.

- Calculate the perimeter and area of simple compound shapes that can be split into rectangles.

- Appreciate different times around the world.

Teacher note

- The children will require a ruler during the written assessment.
- Remind children that we do not put a full stop or an 's' on the end of an abbreviated unit (as in 3kg. or 3kgs).

Oral questions

1. Write the abbreviation for millilitre.
2. What does 'cl' stand for?
3. What does 'oz' mean?
4. How many kilometres are about the same as ten miles?
5. Which is more: four litres or a gallon?
6. One thousandth of a metre is?
7. How many kilograms in one tonne?
8. Write 3.49m in centimetres.
9. Write 250 grams in kilograms.
10. Write 1 centimetre in metres.

Answers

1.	**ml**	6.	**1mm**
2.	**centilitre**	7.	**1000**
3.	**ounce**	8.	**349cm**
4.	**16**	9.	**0.25kg**
5.	**gallon**	10.	**0.01m**

1 Suggest something you would measure in:

a. litres — **e.g. water**   c. pints — **e.g. beer**

b. millimetres — **e.g. insect**   d. ounces — **e.g. butter**

2 Which unit might you use to measure the:

a. width of the Atlantic Ocean? — **kilometres (or miles)**   c. height of a tree? — **metres (or feet)**

b. weight of a 10p piece? — **grams (or ounces)**   d. weight of a bus? — **tonnes (or tons)**

3 Approximately how much are these scales showing?

a. **40kg**

b. **1.2 pints**

c. **2.75 l**

d. **0.65kg**

4 Write some units of measurement you might find in:

a. a kitchen — **e.g. pints, ounces**

b. a chemist's shop — **e.g. millilitres, milligrams**

Name: _____   Date: _____

1.	6.
2.	7.
3.	8.
4.	9.
5.	10.

1 Suggest something you would measure in:

   a. litres   c. pints

   b. millimetres   d. ounces

2 Which unit might you use to measure the:

   a. width of the
      Atlantic Ocean?   c. height of a tree?

   b. weight of a 10p piece?   d. weight of a bus?

3 Approximately how much are these scales showing?

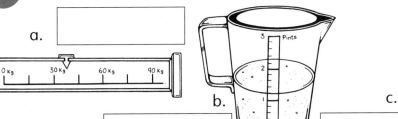

a.

b.

c.

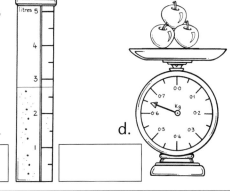

d.

4 Write some units of measurement you might find in:

   a. a kitchen

   b. a chemist's shop

Activity sheet questions

- Use, read and write standard metric units (km, m, cm, mm, kg, g, l, ml, cl), including their abbreviations, and relationships between them.
  Convert smaller to larger units (e.g. m to km, cm or mm to m, g to kg, ml to 1) and vice versa.
  Know imperial units (mile, pint, gallon, lb, oz).
  Know rough equivalents of lb and kg, oz and g, miles and km, litres and pints or gallons.
- Suggest suitable units and measuring equipment to estimate or measure length, mass or capacity.
  Record estimates and readings from scales to a suitable degree of accuracy.

Written

1–3
- **Calculate the perimeter and area of simple compound shapes that can be split into rectangles.**

4
- **Appreciate different times around the world.**

Teacher note

- The children will require a ruler during this assessment.
- Children often confuse area and perimeter. This can result from moving too quickly to the formula l x b for finding area with insufficient time given to developing a sense of what area is. An added confusion is that both area and perimeter can be found by using the lengths of the sides only, in the case of rectangles by adding four of them or multiplying two.

Answers

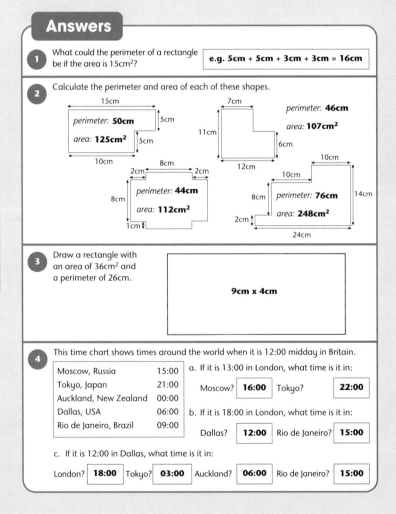

1 What could the perimeter of a rectangle be if the area is 15cm²?

e.g. 5cm + 5cm + 3cm + 3cm = 16cm

2 Calculate the perimeter and area of each of these shapes.

15cm
perimeter: **50cm**
area: **125cm²**
5cm
5cm
10cm

7cm
perimeter: **46cm**
area: **107cm²**
11cm
6cm
12cm

8cm
2cm
2cm
perimeter: **44cm**
area: **112cm²**
8cm
1cm

10cm
10cm
8cm
perimeter: **76cm**
area: **248cm²**
14cm
2cm
24cm

3 Draw a rectangle with an area of 36cm² and a perimeter of 26cm.

9cm x 4cm

4 This time chart shows times around the world when it is 12:00 midday in Britain.

Moscow, Russia	15:00
Tokyo, Japan	21:00
Auckland, New Zealand	00:00
Dallas, USA	06:00
Rio de Janeiro, Brazil	09:00

a. If it is 13:00 in London, what time is it in:

Moscow? **16:00** Tokyo? **22:00**

b. If it is 18:00 in London, what time is it in:

Dallas? **12:00** Rio de Janeiro? **15:00**

c. If it is 12:00 in Dallas, what time is it in:

London? **18:00** Tokyo? **03:00** Auckland? **06:00** Rio de Janeiro? **15:00**

Name: _____   Date: _____

1 What could the perimeter of a rectangle be if the area is 15cm²?

[   ]

2 Calculate the perimeter and area of each of these shapes.

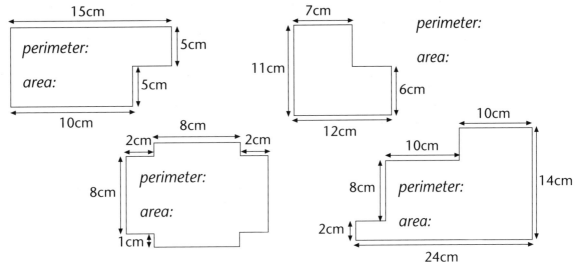

15cm

perimeter:

area:

5cm

5cm

10cm

7cm

perimeter:

area:

11cm

6cm

12cm

8cm

2cm   2cm

8cm

perimeter:

area:

1cm

10cm

10cm

8cm   perimeter:

area:

14cm

2cm

24cm

3 Draw a rectangle with an area of 36cm² and a perimeter of 26cm.

4 This time chart shows times around the world when it is 12:00 midday in Britain.

Moscow, Russia	15:00
Tokyo, Japan	21:00
Auckland, New Zealand	00:00
Dallas, USA	06:00
Rio de Janeiro, Brazil	09:00

a. If it is 13:00 in London, what time is it in:

Moscow? [   ]   Tokyo? [   ]

b. If it is 18:00 in London, what time is it in:

Dallas? [   ]   Rio de Janeiro? [   ]

c. If it is 12:00 in Dallas, what time is it in:

London? [   ] Tokyo? [   ] Auckland? [   ] Rio de Janeiro? [   ]

Shape and space

Activity sheet questions

Written
1–3

Classify quadrilaterals, using criteria such as parallel sides, equal angles, equal sides…

- Describe and visualise properties of solid shapes such as parallel or perpendicular faces or edges.
- Make shapes with increasing accuracy.
- Visualise 3D shapes from 2D drawings and identify different nets for a closed cube.
- Recognise where a shape will be after reflection:
  – in a mirror line touching the shape at a point (sides of shape not necessarily parallel or perpendicular to the mirror line)
  – in two mirror lines at right angles (sides of shape all parallel or perpendicular to the mirror line).
  Recognise where a shape will be after two translations.
- Read and plot co-ordinates in all four quadrants.
- Recognise and estimate angles.
  Use a protractor to measure and draw acute and obtuse angles to the nearest degree.
  Check that the sum of the angles of a triangle is 180°: for example, by measuring or paper folding.
  Calculate angles in a triangle or around a point.
  Recognise where a shape will be after a rotation through 90° about one of its

Teacher note

- A 'quadrilateral' is a 4-sided figure.
- Trapeziums, quadrilaterals with one set of parallel lines, can be both symmetrical and non-symmetrical.

Answers

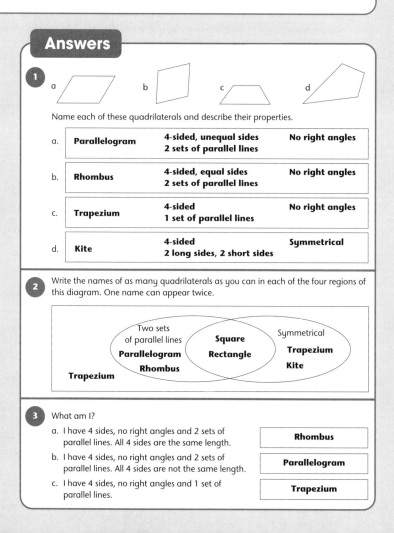

1

a   b   c   d

Name each of these quadrilaterals and describe their properties.

a.	**Parallelogram**	4-sided, unequal sides 2 sets of parallel lines	**No right angles**
b.	**Rhombus**	4-sided, equal sides 2 sets of parallel lines	**No right angles**
c.	**Trapezium**	4-sided 1 set of parallel lines	**No right angles**
d.	**Kite**	4-sided 2 long sides, 2 short sides	**Symmetrical**

2 Write the names of as many quadrilaterals as you can in each of the four regions of this diagram. One name can appear twice.

Two sets of parallel lines · Symmetrical

Square
Rectangle

Parallelogram
Rhombus

Trapezium
Kite

Trapezium

3 What am I?

a. I have 4 sides, no right angles and 2 sets of parallel lines. All 4 sides are the same length.

Rhombus

b. I have 4 sides, no right angles and 2 sets of parallel lines. All 4 sides are not the same length.

Parallelogram

c. I have 4 sides, no right angles and 1 set of parallel lines.

Trapezium

Name: _____ Date: _____

1

a   b   c   d

Name each of these quadrilaterals and describe their properties.

a.

b.

c.

d.

2 Write the names of as many quadrilaterals as you can in each of the four regions of this diagram. One name can appear twice.

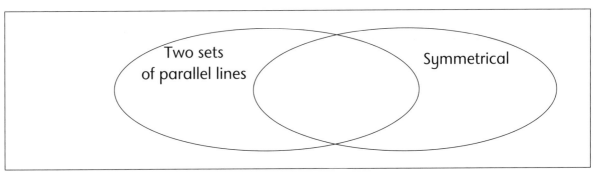

Two sets of parallel lines   Symmetrical

3 What am I?

a. I have 4 sides, no right angles and 2 sets of parallel lines. All 4 sides are the same length.

b. I have 4 sides, no right angles and 2 sets of parallel lines. All 4 sides are not the same length.

c. I have 4 sides, no right angles and 1 set of parallel lines.

Activity sheet questions

Classify quadrilaterals, using criteria such as parallel sides, equal angles, equal sides…

Written

1–2
- **Describe and visualise properties of solid shapes such as parallel or perpendicular faces or edges.**

3–5
- **Make shapes with increasing accuracy.**
  Visualise 3D shapes from 2D drawings and identify different nets for a closed cube.

- Recognise where a shape will be after reflection:
  – in a mirror line touching the shape at a point (sides of shape not necessarily parallel or perpendicular to the mirror line)
  – in two mirror lines at right angles (sides of shape all parallel or perpendicular to the mirror line).
  Recognise where a shape will be after two translations.

- Read and plot co-ordinates in all four quadrants.

- Recognise and estimate angles.
  Use a protractor to measure and draw acute and obtuse angles to the nearest degree.
  Check that the sum of the angles of a triangle is 180°: for example, by measuring or paper folding.
  Calculate angles in a triangle or around a point.
  Recognise where a shape will be after a rotation through 90° about one of its vertices.

Teacher note

- Children will need 5 multilink or centicubes each for question 5.
- Some children find visualising 3D shapes from 2D drawings quite difficult. Encourage them to hold a cube with a vertical edge towards them when trying to draw cubes on isometric paper.

Answers

1 Complete this table.

	Cube	Cuboid	Cylinder	Sphere	Hemisphere	Triangular prism	Tetrahedron
Faces	6	6	3	1	2	5	4
Edges	12	12	2	0	1	9	6
Vertices	8	8	0	0	0	6	4

2 Write the names of some shapes under each heading.

More edges than faces	More faces than edges
e.g. cube, cuboid, square-based pyramid	e.g. cone, cylinder, sphere

3 Which of these nets could be folded to make a closed box?

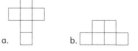

a.   b.   c.

a and c

4 How many cubes are needed to build this shape?

9

5 Stick 5 cubes together to make a shape. Draw your shape on the grid.

Name: _____ Date: _____

---

1 Complete this table.

	Cube	Cuboid	Cylinder	Sphere	Hemisphere	Triangular prism	Tetrahedron
Faces							
Edges							
Vertices							

---

2 Write the names of some shapes under each heading.

More edges than faces	More faces than edges

---

3 Which of these nets could be folded to make a closed box?

a.

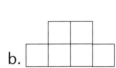
b.

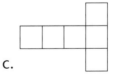
c.

---

4 How many cubes are needed to build this shape?

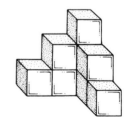

---

5 Stick 5 cubes together to make a shape. Draw your shape on the grid.

Activity sheet questions

○ Describe and visualise properties of solid shapes such as parallel or perpendicular faces or edges.
Classify quadrilaterals, using criteria such as parallel sides, equal angles, equal sides …

○ Make shapes with increasing accuracy.

○ Visualise 3D shapes from 2D drawings and identify different nets for a closed cube.

Written

1–2

● **Recognise where a shape will be after reflection:**
  – in a mirror line touching the shape at a point (sides of shape not necessarily parallel or perpendicular to the mirror line)

3–4

  – in two mirror lines at right angles (sides of shape all parallel or perpendicular to the mirror line).
Recognise where a shape will be after two translations.

○ Read and plot co-ordinates in all four quadrants.

○ Recognise and estimate angles.
Use a protractor to measure and draw acute and obtuse angles to the nearest degree.
Check that the sum of the angles of a triangle is 180°: for example, by measuring or paper folding.
Calculate angles in a triangle or around a point.
Recognise where a shape will be after a rotation through 90° about one of its vertices.

Teacher note

● Provide children with tracing paper to fold over or a mirror to check.

Answers

1 How many lines of reflective symmetry do these shapes have?

a. Square — **4**   c. Regular pentagon — **5**

b. Regular hexagon — **6**   d. Regular octagon — **8**

2 Draw the reflection of these shapes.

3 Use the mirror lines to complete these patterns.

4 Use the mirror lines to reflect these shapes.

Name: _____   Date: _____

Shape and space

---

1 How many lines of reflective symmetry do these shapes have?

    a. Square

    b. Regular hexagon

    c. Regular pentagon

    d. Regular octagon

---

2 Draw the reflection of these shapes.

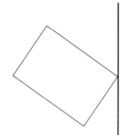

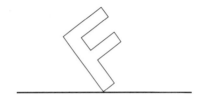

---

3 Use the mirror lines to complete these patterns.

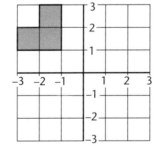

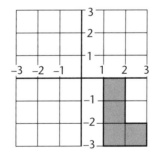

---

4 Use the mirror lines to reflect these shapes.

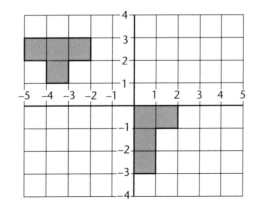

© Folens (copiable page)   MATHS WEEKLY ASSESSMENT: *Book 6*

Shape and space

Activity sheet questions

- Describe and visualise properties of solid shapes such as parallel or perpendicular faces or edges.
  Classify quadrilaterals, using criteria such as parallel sides, equal angles, equal sides …
- Make shapes with increasing accuracy.
- Visualise 3D shapes from 2D drawings and identify different nets for a closed cube.
- Recognise where a shape will be after reflection:
  – in a mirror line touching the shape at a point (sides of shape not necessarily parallel or perpendicular to the mirror line)
  – in two mirror lines at right angles (sides of shape all parallel or perpendicular to the mirror line).

**Written
1–3**

- **Recognise where a shape will be after two translations.**
- **Read and plot co-ordinates in all four quadrants.**
- Recognise and estimate angles.
  Use a protractor to measure and draw acute and obtuse angles to the nearest degree.
  Check that the sum of the angles of a triangle is 180°: for example, by measuring or paper folding.
  Calculate angles in a triangle or around a point.
  Recognise where a shape will be after a rotation through 90° about one of its

Teacher note

- Children can memorise such phrases as 'along the corridor and up the stairs' or 'x is a cross, x is across' to help them remember the order in which we read and write co-ordinates.
- Children will need yellow- and red-coloured pens or pencils for question 3.

Answers

1 a. Translate this shape 3 units down and 3 units to the right.   b. Translate this shape 4 units to the left and 2 units up.

c. Write the co-ordinates of each vertex of the original shapes and of the translated shapes.

| Original: | (–1,1), (–3,1), (–3,2), (–2,2), (–2,3), (–1,3) |
| Translated: | (2,–2), (0,–2), (0,–1), (1,–1), (1,0), (2,0) |

| Original: | (1,0), (2,0), (2,–2), (3,–2), (3,–3), (1,–3) |
| Translated: | (–3,2), (–2,2), (–2,0), (–1, 0), (–1,–1), (–3,–1) |

2 Translate shape **a** 7 units to the right and 5 units down.
Translate shape **b** 4 units up and 2 units to the left.

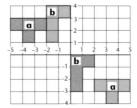

3 Which of the white shapes are translations or reflections of the shaded shape?
Colour the translations yellow and the reflections red.

(Y = yellow, R = red)

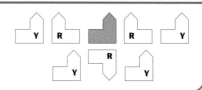

Shape and space

1   a. Translate this shape 3 units down and 3 units to the right.

b. Translate this shape 4 units to the left and 2 units up.

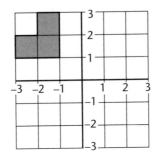

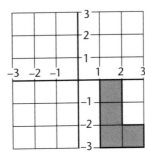

c. Write the co-ordinates of each vertex of the original shapes and of the translated shapes.

Original:	Original:
Translated:	Translated:

2 Translate shape **a** 7 units to the right and 5 units down.
Translate shape **b** 4 units up and 2 units to the left.

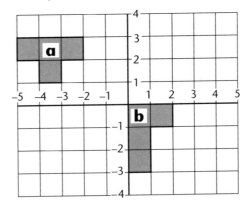

3 Which of the white shapes are translations or reflections of the shaded shape?
Colour the translations yellow and the reflections red.

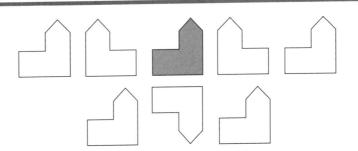

Activity sheet questions

- Describe and visualise properties of solid shapes such as parallel or perpendicular faces or edges.
  Classify quadrilaterals, using criteria such as parallel sides, equal angles, equal sides…
- Make shapes with increasing accuracy.
- Visualise 3D shapes from 2D drawings and identify different nets for a closed cube.
- Recognise where a shape will be after reflection:
  - in a mirror line touching the shape at a point (sides of shape not necessarily parallel or perpendicular to the mirror line)
  - in two mirror lines at right angles (sides of shape all parallel or perpendicular to the mirror line).
  Recognise where a shape will be after two translations.
- Read and plot co-ordinates in all four quadrants.

Written

1 • **Recognise and estimate angles.**

2–3 **Use a protractor to measure and draw acute and obtuse angles to the nearest degree.**

4 **Check that the sum of the angles of a triangle is 180°: for example, by measuring or paper folding.**
Calculate angles in a triangle or around a point.

5 **Recognise where a shape will be after a rotation through 90° about one of its vertices.**

Teacher note

- Children will require a ruler and a protractor. They should be encouraged to draw angles that do not always have a horizontal base, by turning the protractor.

Answers

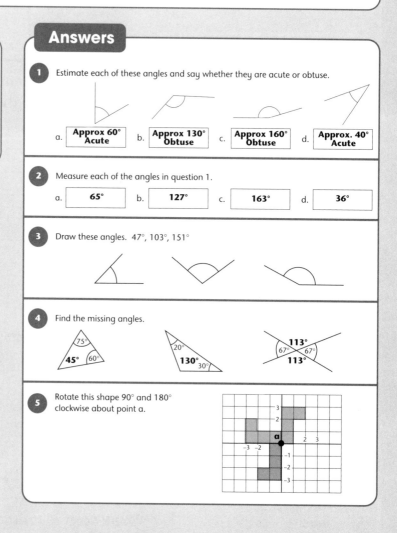

1 Estimate each of these angles and say whether they are acute or obtuse.

a. **Approx 60° Acute** b. **Approx 130° Obtuse** c. **Approx 160° Obtuse** d. **Approx. 40° Acute**

2 Measure each of the angles in question 1.

a. **65°** b. **127°** c. **163°** d. **36°**

3 Draw these angles. 47°, 103°, 151°

4 Find the missing angles.

75°, **45°**, 60°   20°, **130°**, 30°   **113°**, 67°, 67°, **113°**

5 Rotate this shape 90° and 180° clockwise about point a.

Name: _____   Date: _____

1 Estimate each of these angles and say whether they are acute or obtuse.

   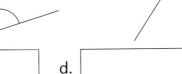

a. [   ]   b. [   ]   c. [   ]   d. [   ]

2 Measure each of the angles in question 1.

a. [   ]   b. [   ]   c. [   ]   d. [   ]

3 Draw these angles. 47°, 103°, 151°

4 Find the missing angles.

 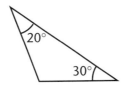 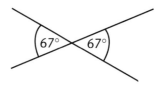

5 Rotate this shape 90° and 180° clockwise about point a.

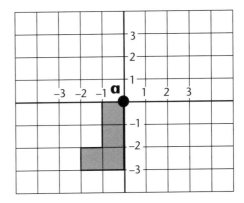

Record sheet

Names	Assessment No.						Number of answers																											
	1	2	3	4	5	6	7	8	9	10	11	12	13	14	15	16	17	18	19	20	21	22	23	24	25	26	27	28	29	30	31	32	33	34